To Mary,
In complete contr

tes
& Insulin, for
different
Good wishes,
Clare.

High Country Legacy

The Aspinalls of Mt Aspiring Station

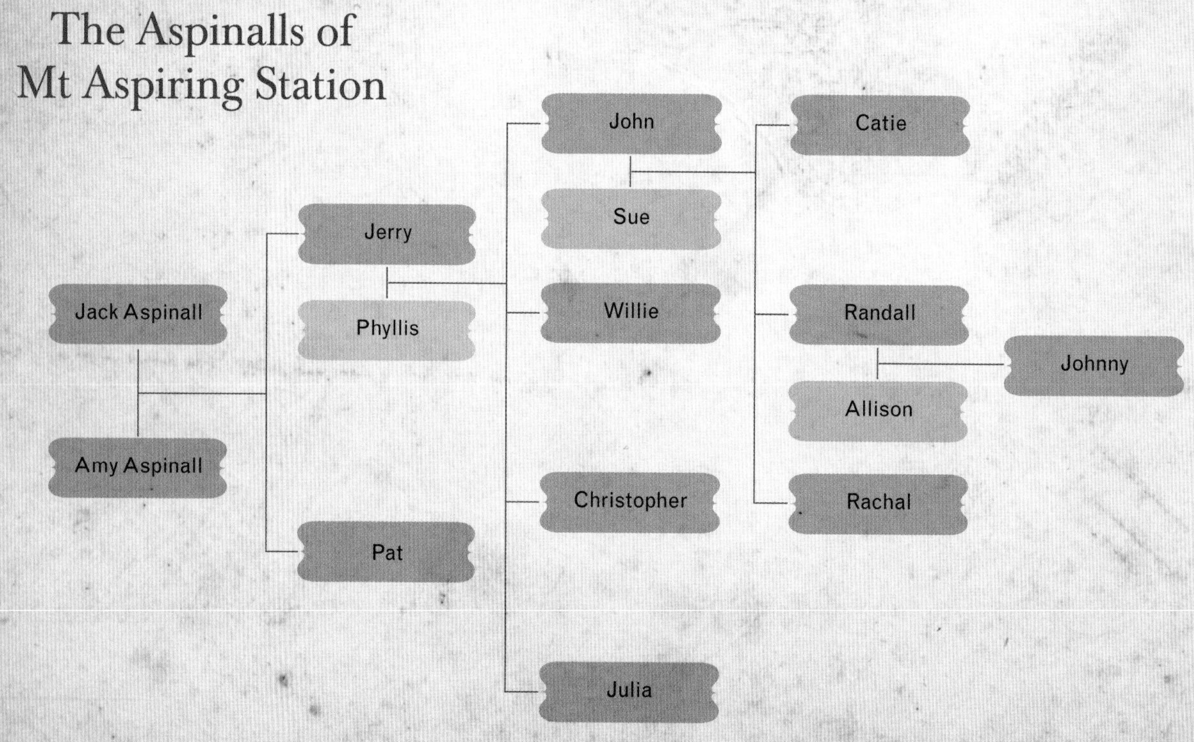

High Country Legacy

Four generations of Aspinalls at Mt Aspiring Station

Alex Hedley

HarperCollins*Publishers*

HarperCollins*Publishers*

First published in 2012
by HarperCollins*Publishers (New Zealand) Limited*
PO Box 1, Shortland Street, Auckland 1140

HarperCollins*Publishers*
31 View Road, Glenfield, Auckland 0627, New Zealand
Level 13, 201 Elizabeth Street, Sydney, NSW 2000, Australia
A 53, Sector 57, Noida, UP, India
77–85 Fulham Palace Road, London W6 8JB, United Kingdom
2 Bloor Street East, 20th floor, Toronto, Ontario M4W 1A8, Canada
10 East 53rd Street, New York, NY 10022, USA

National Library of New Zealand Cataloguing-in-Publication Data
Hedley, Alex.
High Country legacy : four generations of Aspinalls at Mt.
Aspiring Station / Alex Hedley.
ISBN 978-1-77554-004-5
1. Aspinall family. 2. Mount Aspiring Station (N.Z.)—History.
I. Title.
636.010922—dc 23

ISBN: 978 1 77554 004 5

Cover and internals design by Cheryl Rowe
All cover and internal photographs by author and from Aspinall family, except where mentioned.

Publisher: Bill Honeybone
Printed by Geon, Auckland

‘Only he can understand what a farm is, what a country is, who shall have sacrificed part of himself to his farm or country, fought to save it, struggled to make it beautiful. Only then will the love of farm or country fill his heart.’

— Antoine de Saint-Exupéry (1900–44)

Mt Aspiring Station is in the mountainous backblocks of Otago, between Lake Wanaka and the Southern Alps. It runs on both sides of an ice-fed river called the Matukituki, in a deep, U-shaped valley formed over thousands of years by glacial excavation. The Aspinall family have farmed sheep and cattle here since 1920. Their homestead sits just south-east of the confluence of the east and west branches of the river, the last occupied home before the head of the valley and Te Wahipounamu, South West New Zealand UNESCO World Heritage Area, New Zealand's most pristine natural wilderness.

This book is dedicated to John Henry Aspinall
of Mt Aspiring Station, 1951–2011, farmer,
hunter, fisherman, tramper and conservationist.

The schist rock wall of Aspiring hut.

Contents

Introduction

From the valley to the sky

'Sustainable management will not be achieved by rules, regulations, legislation or plans. It is achieved by those working the land with sweaty brows and dirty hands.' These words are by the late John Aspinall of Mt Aspiring Station, a towering figure in the story of the New Zealand high country. It's a quote that has echoed around the mountains of the South Island for some time, and it resonates as much today as it ever has.

John's grandfather, John 'Jack' Aspinall, arrived here in 1920 to a ramshackle homestead bound on all sides by a hostile and lonely landscape, ruled by the whims of nature, and infested with rabbits and deer. Two generations of tough Scottish Highlanders had lived here before him, eventually abandoning the land to the river that took the lives of three of their kin. It was known as a godforsaken place, shrugged off by the first settlers in Otago as a farming wasteland. But as Jack Aspinall rode towards the last station in the valley he looked up from his yoke high to the mountains, spellbound by their beauty.

This is the story of Mt Aspiring Station and the Matukituki Valley, from its darkest, primitive beginnings to its success at the modern intersection of environmental, recreational and economic sustainability. It's about custodianship of New Zealand's high country and a deep love and understanding of the land. It's also about life growing up in an isolated world, ruled by the elements and a capricious river. Three generations of Aspinall children were schooled by correspondence here, finishing their lessons early to be out in their 10,000-hectare playground. Their education goes deeper than any government curriculum, and can't be taught in a classroom. Their understanding of the land is in their blood, and they have deep respect for its potential, its limits and its vulnerability.

In the days when the Mt Aspiring Station homestead was in a dark corner of the valley, 'under the shadow of the avalanche', the Matukituki River and its unpredictable temperament dictated everyday life with a mighty hand. For some it was a constant source of dread. And the valley could be a melancholy place, surrounded on all sides by peaks of perpetual snow and ice, the ground beneath the homestead frozen solid

Mt Aspiring Station woolshed.

for months on end. 'It is hard to comprehend in today's world of swift transport and communication the hardships that the Aspinall family endured over the years,' a close friend of the family once said, for there was little contact with the outside world this far down the valley. But through isolation came the skills of self-reliance and sustainability, from the homestead to beyond the bush line, and with it also a unique attitude to outsiders, the 'loopies', as they were known.

Looming above the mist to the west of the station is Mount Aspiring/Tititea, at 3033 metres the highest peak in New Zealand outside Aoraki/Mount Cook National Park. Without any prior knowledge of mountaineering, Jack Aspinall was one of the first to climb Mount Aspiring, and no history of ascending the 'Matterhorn of the South' could ever begin without mention of the station at its feet. The long association with the alpine and hunting communities and the devotion with which the Aspinalls welcomed them to the valley is the remarkable overture to the story of land access this book also hopes to tell. In the early days only a handful of pioneering climbers would visit after the thaw but, 100 years on, Mt Aspiring Station receives an estimated 80,000 visitors every year.

In 1957 John's parents, Jerry and Phyllis, voluntarily surrendered 20,235 hectares (50,000 acres) to the Crown to help form Mount Aspiring National Park, the beauty

The back country road to Mt Aspiring Station, beside the Matukituki River.

of which needs no introduction. They befriended all who came through the valley, receiving anyone brave enough to cross the river with a famous high country welcome. It is exemplary of farming on the doorstep of a national park, without the need for 'rules and regulations', as John so keenly put it.

When John's short battle with leukaemia ended in November 2011, condolences from all corners of the high country world flooded in, saluting him as a 'guardian of the environment', a 'champion of public access' and 'the beau idéal of a high country farmer'. His death was not only felt throughout the entire farming community, his departure was hailed as a national tragedy. With John's passing, his son Randall and his wife Allison, along with John's widow Sue, are now faced with the challenge of continuing to champion the values of the high country those before them worked so hard to forge. Their future and the future of the newest member of the Aspinall family, John 'Johnny' Aspinall, lies among this station's ancient hills and the short-tempered river at its heart, from the valley to the sky.

It is hoped those values the Aspinalls have imparted on all the valley's visitors and station hands might in some small way be preserved, their message to New Zealand passed on, for the challenge is great but the vision aspiring.

The upper reaches of the West Matukituki Valley.

Clockwise from top left: Jerry Aspinall; Allison and Randall Aspinall with their son Johnny; Christopher Aspinall; Julia Aspinall; John and Sue Aspinall with their children (from left) Randall, Rachal and Catie; Sue Aspinall; Amy and Jack Aspinall with their children Jerry and Pat; Willie Aspinall.

APR • 67

The swing bridge across the West Matukituki River.

Opposite: Two unnamed peaks opposite Raspberry Hut in the West Matukituki Valley.

{ Aspinall country }

If you follow the back country road out of Wanaka at night, around the frozen bends of the Glendhu bluffs, over the cattle stop beneath Treble Cone ski field, the road flattens out into the Matukituki Valley and the darkness becomes thicker still. Past the bogs and mires of the river's wetlands the mountains grow taller, an amphitheatre of shadows drawing in on both sides. The road continues past Black Peak and the streams issued from its folds before the road transforms into a sweeping arc around Niger Peak, and on a small terrace south of the river sits number 3945, Mt Aspiring Station homestead, the last residence before the great dividing range.

On a cool autumn night there's a silence over the Matukituki Valley as the frost builds and a drifting fog over the river ebbs down the valley. Soon the veil starts to dissolve, unnoticed, and almost like a trick of the eye a stencil of a craggy range peels back, 2000 metres above the homestead, a pin-sharp line against a lightening sky. A shelter belt by the gate shakes to life against a lowering wind, a cool breath exhales over the valley from the Alps to the west. This morning the wind is faint, but ask anyone who has spent time in the Matukituki and they'll soon tell you 'it sure can blow'. A huntaway's bark pierces the air. From a row of concrete kennels chains rattle and the other dogs soon join in. High above them the points of the range appear dipped in a sullen orange, inching down the ramparts of rock and tussock. On the other side of the valley great sheaths of light puncture between the peaks; the light is ever-changing in the valley, and it's this natural display those who have lived here often miss the most.

A desk-lamp flickers on in the station office and Randall Aspinall sits down to survey the landscape of ridges, ribs and spurs slowly revealing itself outside the window. And he notes the weather, beholds his land, as his family have done every morning for almost one hundred years. A pair of paradise shelducks fly high above the grey boulders of the river, before the mountains claim back their silhouettes against the dripping beech forests. To the west, a series of peaks converge in the distance, the valley narrowing to a wilderness of forests, ice and mountains. The ancient glaciers on Mount Avalanche begin to glow white, and beyond them looms the greatest peak this side of Mount Cook, and the station's namesake, Mount Aspiring.

Beside the old heat-storage range in the homestead kitchen, adjacent to the office, two young shepherds sit in Swazi outdoor gear having their breakfast. The Aspinall family have always employed a single worker at the station, usually a young boy or girl just out of school in their first year of full-time farming. Because of the isolation, the shepherds live at the station and eat with the family. The workers' quarters are down a narrow concrete path, past the glasshouse and through a gate beside a small wooded area of dogwoods, maples

Mt Aspiring Station homestead beneath Niger Peak, the last residence in the Matukituki Valley before the great dividing range.

The new Mt Aspiring Station homestead, built of Oamaru stone in 1969.

and japonicas. There's always a stack of well-worn manuka hill-sticks by the door, and beside them usually at least one pair of sodden tramping boots.

Over the years the shepherds who came to Aspiring would do so with varying levels of ability and fitness — some of them with no experience at all, 'pretty green', the Aspinalls would call them. Some kept coming back for more, and some ran to the hills. Generally, though, they've always been keen to learn, and they soon build the courage required for the top mustering beats. This week Randall has two shepherds, Monique King from Makarora, at the head of Lake Wanaka, and Struan Mehrtens from Springfield, in the foothills of Canterbury. Struan is on a break from university at Lincoln, from where he drove down the island to spend some time in the mountains. He enjoys the challenge that comes with farming and hunting at altitude, and he'll certainly find what he's looking for here at Aspiring.

Mt Aspiring Station takes in the land from the homestead up to the haybarns at Cameron Flat, from where it forks in two, as does the river, known as the west

The uppermost boundary of Mt Aspiring Station above the West Matukituki Valley.
From left: Glenfinnan Peak, the ridge leading to Fog Peak, and Sharks Tooth Peak.

and east branches. Surrounding the station up both branches, at every angle, are foreboding peaks and vertical waterfalls, feeding the two rivers. Behind the homestead, the station's southern frontier is a range split by fissures, punctuated by summits of sharp teeth and spires, and littered with scree, moraine boulders and glacial rubble down to the river.

Along the boundary are several major peaks, from Glenfinnan, nearly 2000 metres up behind the homestead, to Mount Tyndall, 500 metres higher again. Between Glenfinnan and Mount Tyndall rise the summits of Fog Peak, Sharks Tooth Peak and Craigroyston Peak, and between the grazeable faces are gorges lined with beech and bracken, forming several natural fencelines. The station continues across a face above the old possumer's hut at Raspberry Creek, beneath the range recess of the Shotover Saddle and beyond the Brides Veil Waterfall to Red Rock. From here a stream trickles back to the valley floor near the twin chimneys of Cascade Hut, an old alpine cabin on the edge of the forest. Then, tracking back east, on the other side of the river, the station includes all the terraced country between Big Creek and the ice-shorn cliffs known as Hells Gate, but dark beech forests spilling down from the slopes create the formidable station boundary and the entrance to some of the highest summits in the area — Glengyle, Rob Roy and Homestead peaks.

Waterfalls below the Rob Roy Glacier.
Image courtesy of Kieran Scott.

On the edge of the forest there is a swing bridge over the river to the Rob Roy walk, leading into a world of vast hanging glaciers and vertical waterfalls, an incredible display of the inherent forces at work on the landscape around Mt Aspiring Station. Further east down the valley another swing bridge links the two banks of the river at MacPherson Creek, where the old Scottish crofter Duncan Macpherson and his family used to live, now the site of the Otago Boys' High School lodge. From here the stock can make their way around Homestead Peak and into the east branch of the valley. The station extends up the east branch until its boundary at Glacier Burn, where the beech forest closes in on the river.

Randall Aspinall continues to run approximately the same numbers of stock his father John ran at Aspiring: 3500 ewes, 700 two-tooth ewes and 920 hoggets spread across the wide faces beneath the scree, 520 Hereford-Angus cross cows free to graze the valley from the homestead to Cascade Hut, producing 450 calves, 60 per cent of which are sold at weaning time, with 100 replacement heifer calves and 100 replacement 18-month-old heifers remaining for the winter; 216 mixed-age steers run on high and rough ground until they are four years old, 20 bulls, 60 rams — and 20 beehives in a paddock below the homestead. Mt Aspiring's steers, the young castrated males, spend the summer in the hanging valleys of mountainous Mill Creek block, and they winter on Cattle Face, high above the east branch of the river, between Glacier Burn and Junction Flat. Below Cattle Face, the Matukituki River snakes around to join the Kitchener, draining the eastern aspects of Popes Nose and Mount Avalanche over Turnbull Thomson Falls and Aspiring Flats. From Cattle Face the old Aspiring boundary used to extend from the bush line to Albert Burn Saddle, then to the headwaters of Minaret Burn, before circling back south along the high ridge above the eastern hanging valley and encompassing everything in between — including Mount Eostre and Dragonfly Peak — before linking back over the transition from alpine tussock herb fields to the beech forests and eventually the steep descent back to the homestead.

On the wall next to Randall's desk is a handwritten list of dog training exercises: Zac needs to keep working on his 'stand' call, especially at a distance, and while Jade needs a confidence boost, Tan and Joe both need to work on their manners (they are prone to barking and stirring on the truck). Tyke just needs to get used to whistle calls, especially for 'sit down' and 'wayleggo'. It's a new team, with a new master, yet Randall John Aspinall is the fourth generation of Aspinalls to farm at Aspiring and it won't take long for them to find their feet. Randall moved into the homestead with his wife Allison during the winter of 2010 after working for eight years as a farm consultant in Invercargill. And although he has a good head for the tough economics of farming in the twenty-first century, by his own admission he's still coming to terms with some of the more hands-on skills required for this rugged mountain country. Past the office, through the dining room and into the kitchen, there's a note pinned on the cork notice board beside the fridge, with bold letters at the top:

> SHEARING: Before they start the machines the house needs to have the kitchen water turned off. Maybe you could use one element on the electric stove but NOT the oven. Use the old oven if need be. The electric jug is another NONO and any other thermostat appliance. Cook ahead of time for your lunch and tea. Think simple. Cold meat/savs/pizza/quiche for our guys' lunch. You can fry spuds but just be watchful of the meters. Keeping the kitchen fire going to heat water is a good idea.

The note was left by Randall's mother, Sue Aspinall, who lived for 33 years with her husband John, at the homestead where they brought up their three children, Catie, Randall and Rachal. Sue lived here longer than any other woman this far up the valley, and although she now lives in Wanaka she's regularly seen driving up the Aspiring Road, lending a hand with shifting stock where she can, weeding the well-tended garden, and providing essential practical tips to keep the homestead running, not least on the temperamental power supply from the waterfall above the Niger Creek canyon.

Fog drifting down the Matukituki Valley beyond the homestead buried in the trees.

Allison and Randall Aspinall with John 'Johnny' Aspinall, the fifth generation of Aspinalls at Mt Aspiring Station.

The 2000-metre-high rocky spire, Sharks Tooth Peak.

Allison Dick met Randall in her home town of Invercargill and, like others before her, she's always mindful that moving into a homestead comes with a set of expectations left by her predecessors. She also came to the station with no previous knowledge of farming animals, but those same predecessors would also come to reassure her that this situation was no first. When Grandma Phyllis, now in her nineties, married Randall's grandfather Jerry in 1950, she had been training as a music teacher: 'Hardly a background for back country farming,' her husband Jerry said. And by her own admission, Phyllis says, 'It was quite a challenge, because I didn't even like animals!' Randall and Allison moved into the homestead earlier than they had anticipated when Randall's father John was diagnosed with a blood-related disease called myelodysplasia. Over time, John's disease progressed to acute myeloid leukaemia, a rare cancer that starts by attacking cells inside bone marrow. On 15 August 2011 John made a note in his diary, saying he had felt the energy drain out of his body and, not long after, on a summer's day in 2011, a high country legend died in Dunedin hospital.

John left behind his mother Phyllis, his two brothers Willie and Christopher, sister Julia, his wife Sue and three children. Despite the suddenness with which nature took its course, Randall had already known his future lay in the Matukituki Valley. 'I was always going to,' Randall says. 'Ever since I was three, I just grew up thinking, "I'm going to end up here."' The Aspinall farm has always gone to the first-born son, and in each case they always grew up with a deep bond to the land, knowing they were going to take over, in line with tradition. But it takes a strong family unit to run a station like this; no one would dare brave it alone.

When Randall's great-grandfather arrived in 1920, Mt Aspiring Station was considered the frontier of pastoral farming in the Dominion, and to no small extent it remains so to this day. It was the furthest-out station in the Wanaka district, it relied on the natural boundaries of a marginal environment, and for decades it fought back those who tried to tame it.

John 'Jack' Aspinall was born into a large family in the industrial town of Preston, Lancashire. At the age of 12 he was required to help support his family and as a result he spent three and a half years as a pastry cook before taking up a job cooking on ocean liners sailing across the Atlantic. He developed an adventurous spirit during his time at sea, one that eventually landed him on a boat bound for Port Chalmers, New Zealand. From 1909 to 1912 Jack cooked on remote sawmill sites, before his reputation as both a cook and handyman took him to Theodore Russell's Cattle Flat Station in

Clockwise from top left: Randall Aspinall with Zac; Allison with Johnny; rock and tussock on Mt Aspiring Station; the Matukituki Valley through Hells Gate.

The glaciers of Mount Avalanche, with Low Peak and Homestead Peak to its left.

the Matukituki Valley. He worked here until he went to war in 1915 as a driver with the New Zealand Artillery. On a leave pass in August 1918 Jack met and married Amy Page from Liverpool, but the following month Jack was gassed on the Western Front, just weeks before the Armistice was signed, and spent the rest of his service time convalescing in England and tending to army stables.

With the decaying bodies and mud of the trenches still fresh in his mind, Jack Aspinall returned to New Zealand with his Liverpudlian war bride Amy in the winter of 1920. With the financial assistance of Theo Russell, Jack purchased the pastoral lease numbers 458, 465 and 468, Mt Aspiring Station. For Amy, a more far-flung and isolated land could never have been imagined. Tales from the Matukituki Valley preceded her: it was so cold in the winter that Jack used to heat up rocks on the stove and put them in his bed; a treacherous river of boulders and quicksand had to be crossed three times to reach the homestead; the thunderous noise of cataracts and avalanches had turned the previous owners deaf; there were mighty red-winged birds tearing holes in the backs of sheep; and there was no contact with the outside world besides the 30 mile trip on horseback to the tiny settlement by the lake. Yet Amy developed a thick skin, and made the best of what she had deep in the Matukituki Valley for the next 30 years.

The Aspinalls moved into the homestead previously lived in by the old crofter Hugh Macpherson (Duncan's uncle), up the east branch of the river, in the shadow of Homestead Peak. They arrived to a cold, damp house, built of odds and sods and rotting timber. The property itself was huge, some 29,000 hectares, but it was unfenced and infested with rabbits. Jack bought the remainder of Duncan Macpherson's sheep and cattle, and then drove a considerable mob on foot over the Lindis Pass, as well as 300 Border Leicester ewes from Oamaru. But the stock soon lived a wild existence at Mount Aspiring while the Aspinalls battled to take control of what little pasture remained. Then, on a winter morning in August, while washing clothes in the nearby creek, the smell of smoke attracted Amy's attention. The chimney was on fire, flames leaping onto the roof's wooden shingles. Jack noticed the tufts of smoke from two miles away where he was rabbiting, but by the time he got back all but the few wedding presents Amy managed to throw out the window and the pile of clothes by the creek was lost. It was a sickening setback for the couple, yet it was to reveal the qualities in them both that would stand against adversity in those days of great isolation.

Jack and Amy used wood from the old sawmill structures to build a bedroom alongside a shed, which became the homestead for the winter. Through it all Amy had been pregnant with their first child, who was born John 'Jerry' Aspinall in Cromwell

Hospital at the end of October 1921. The child was frail, and mother and son didn't return to Aspiring until January, to a new house, simple, but a home nonetheless. Three years later their daughter Lesley arrived on St Patrick's Day 1924 and was instantly nicknamed 'Pat'. The family lived a frugal existence: they ate everything that grew, and the land always came first. The children grew up watching their parents toil in isolation against the environment — heavy rainfall, avalanches, floods, slips, hoar frosts — but it was from this landscape that a tough breed of high country farmer was forged, one with a bloody-minded constitution, and a deep respect for the terms of nature.

Twenty years after Jerry was born, with war again erupting in Europe, Jack Aspinall was diagnosed with a terminal illness and, on the morning of 27 January 1942, he passed away. It may have been sudden, but for his son Jerry, in training at Burnham Military Camp, it could well have saved him from the battlefields of the Western Desert. Jerry stepped into his father's boots at just 20 years old, to take over the running of the station with his mother and younger sister. Eight years later Jerry married Phyllis Manson, and at the same homestead they brought up four children: John, Willie, Christopher and Julia. In 1977 Jerry told his eldest son John it was his turn to be boss: 'Our type of country is young man's country,' he declared, and so Phyllis and Jerry made way for John and his wife Sue Cottrell from Cust in North Canterbury.

One hundred years after Jack Aspinall first rode into the Matukituki Valley, his great-grandson Randall is still there. Phyllis Aspinall has a saying: 'It often happens within families that when one member goes, another small new life appears.' Less than a year after John's death, Randall and Allison have a newborn son, John Aspinall, known by all as 'Johnny'.

There's a pattern of life to the story, and the way the first generations lived has had a profound effect on the values of those taking on the mantle. A web of enduring lessons about living in the back country is passed down from year to year. To understand the future of this fifth generation of high country custodians, and the cloth from which he is made, the story of his forebears and those even before the Aspinalls must be told, for their story is undeniably his; their tragedies, their failures, their virtues, all are important to understand the present and the future at Mt Aspiring Station. For 'one learns to read the high country and its moods,' John used to say, but it takes time.

The rocky track over Mt Aspiring Station to the head of the West Matukituki.

Top row, from left: An early sightseer in the Matukituki; the Aspinall family in the 1960s, (from left) John, Jerry, Julia, Christopher, Willie and Phyllis; Jerry Aspinall with his two sons John and Christopher crossing the Matukituki; William Page Aspinall. Middle: Fording a stream in the Matukituki; John Henry Aspinall, 1952, aged 8 months old; Willie Aspinall on Chum the horse alongside a visiting friend; the Kershaws going to mind Aspiring Hut at Christmas. Bottom: Shifting sheep through the river; the Matukituki from the slopes of the Shotover Saddle; the old signpost at Cameron Flat; Jerry Aspinall with shorn ewes in the yards. *Images courtesy of the Aspinall family collection.*

CAMERON FLAT
WANAKA
28
ROB ROY GLACIER
WALKING TRACK
Mt ASPIRING HUT
FIREPLACE
3/4

Mt Aspiring Station shepherd Monique King.

Paradise shelducks in the East Matukituki.

The old Mt Aspiring Station homestead meat safe for the dog tucker.

Opposite: Duncan Macpherson's original west branch homestead, Christmas 1906. Nothing of the homestead remains today.

Lone shielings

When the first Europeans came to the South Island in the early 1850s the accessible pastoral runs were taken up on a first-in, best-dressed basis. Farmers and their flocks soon spread across the arable plains, until by the later part of the nineteenth century those arriving with similar ambitions and lesser means had to look further, beyond the frontiers, towards the distant mountains. First they came to the foothills, and then to the basins and lakes to where the mountains drained their melting ice and snow. From here they pushed further still, to the heads of the lakes and the gorges of the big rivers, until they could go no further. All that lay ahead was sheer masses of impenetrable mountains.

Those who had blazed the trail for the farmers into the interior were government surveyors. The first of these to enter the Hawea and Wanaka region was the long-serving colonist, able surveyor and no less talented artist John Turnbull Thomson. In 1856 Thomson was appointed Chief Surveyor for the Province of Otago, and given the enormous task of surveying the blank spaces of Otago and Southland, an area almost the size of Scotland. In telling the modern history of Mt Aspiring Station, you could say it all began with Thomson, for in 1857 he became the first European to lay eyes on the incredible panorama of the Upper Clutha Basin. From the same vantage point, on top of the mountain he had at first named Black Knob, Thomson also saw a 'lofty conical peak' 40 miles distant, to which he gave the name Mount Aspiring. He later renamed his vantage point 'Grandview Mountain', and it's from here one of his most famous paintings revealed what he saw: 'lakes blue and narrow, surrounded by intensive forests reaching to the white gravelly shores, hemmed in by bold and lofty mountains'.

There's some conjecture about the naming of Aspiring, and in recent years there have been observations from Thomson's likely vantage points where Aspiring is barely visible, let alone taking the appearance of a 'lofty conical peak' — in all probability it was Mount Aeolus which Thomson named Aspiring. Either way, the name certainly lends itself to the former, and the name stuck.

The earliest explorers of the South Island, according to tradition, were the Hawea and Te Rapuwai people, and the Waitaha — the moa-hunters. Early Maori settlement at the bottom of the Matukituki Valley is evident especially around the swamps and nesting grounds, where the outlines of ancient gardens can be made out. There's also a circular stone at West Wanaka Station that some suggest was used for cleaning the fat off moa skins, and greenstone artefacts have been found near the head of the Arawhata River below the western side of Mount Aspiring, suggesting Maori once used the Matukituki Valley to access the greenstone waters of Westland. But Maori

Ewen Cameron's Glenfinnan Station in 1883, not far from the present Mt Aspiring Station homestead.

tracks weren't obvious to European explorers, and navigable passage to the West Coast remained steeped in mystery.

Jollie, Young and Pyke, on their expedition of 1859, were the first Europeans to visit Lake Wanaka itself, deployed as surveyors by an Otago provincial government anxious to plot a route through the mountains to the West Coast. As they skirted the lake's western shores they came to its meeting place with the Matukituki River, and followed it up the west branch some way, with the belief that somewhere in the area there was a Maori path to the Awarua River on the other side of the Alps, but, despite their best efforts, the riddle of the Matukituki remained. In their wake, two years later, came James McKerrow, with his two assistants John Goldie and James Bryce, who quickly became obsessed with the elusive Maori tracks from the mountain lakes to the coast. When the party came to the Matukituki, Goldie recorded what they saw there in a journal addressed to a cousin in Scotland.

> On each side of this river the mountain peaks appear to pierce the sky. As regards the height of these mountains they approach far nearer and are far more worthy of having the appellation bestowed on them which Burns gave to them in Bonnie Scotland. ... I can assure you that the scenery here though wild in its grandeur was beyond anything that I have ever seen for its beauty.

But as the trio from Bonnie Scotland neared the head of the valley, McKerrow wrote of the thunder of the frequent avalanches, their

> overwhelming force displayed in its ruthless track cleft through the forest; where remains of the great trees lie torn and snapped into matchwood. Glacier Dome and Mount Aspiring, enthroned in perpetual ice, bid defiance to the sun and forbid the approach of the beholder, who is spellbound, impressed with awe and veneration at the stupendous forces of nature.

From here they fled from the awful abyss, retreating back down the valley.

At just 28 years of age and fresh from the wilds of Canada, yet another Scottish explorer arrived in New Zealand to survey the pathways of the South Island. In a three-year contract, James Hector was asked by the Otago Government to record the possibility of gold and other minerals, potential for agriculture, and to continue to search for a way to the coast. Late in 1862, Hector visited the Matukituki Valley, where he noted the presence of the now-extinct South Island kokako, and climbed Black Peak observing what looked to be a gap in the mountains south of Aspiring.

The old crofter Duncan Macpherson at Mt Aspiring Station homestead, originally built by his uncle Hugh Macpherson.

Mr and Mrs Duncan Macpherson and their four children at a picnic on New Year's Day, 1906.
Mrs Macpherson would eventually drown in the Matukituki River.

Some months later, in January 1863, Hector returned and clawed his way deeper into the valley. He set up a base camp at the confluence of the two rivers, and used packhorses as far as Shovel Flat. His team had provisions for six days, but the return journey would ultimately take 17. Reports were published in the *Otago Daily Times* in March telling of their adventure beyond the limit of the woods, encountering 'gorges beset with huge boulders', 'profound ice valleys' and 'rivers kept flooded by continuous rain'. Higher still they passed among blocks of ice and stone, wide glaciers, deep crevasses, and the heavy debris of avalanches falling every 10 minutes. The party had climbed the alpine saddle at the head of the valley, which they named Hector Col, step-cut across the giant Bonar Glacier, and descended to the Waipara–Arawhata confluence to a point where they were within a few miles of the coast. But from here the expedition was beaten back by terrible weather, lack of food and the final gorge of the Waipara. They were demoralized, malnourished, cold and wet. And their story haunted the Matukituki for some 15 years before any serious thought was given to farming in the valley.

The first man to bring sheep into the uppermost reaches of the Matukituki Valley was Ewen Cameron, one of several Scottish Highlanders to brave this inhospitable land

The Russell and Ewing Mill Creek homesteads in 1877.

from 1880 to 1919, facing loneliness and, finally, tragedy. Cameron left his home of Fort William in 1866, and arrived in the Matukituki a man of moderate means with his wife Marion. Cameron built his 'shieling' or small house here, a mud-brick affair along with stable and yard, on the Glenfinnan terrace, taking up runs 458 and 468 in 1877 and calling his holding Genfinnan Station. The *Otago Witness* reported the following at the time of Cameron's tenure:

> It may be safely stated that the term "rough and broken country" applies with more complete application than it does to the Matukituki Valley. So much are the hills cut up about here by deep gulches, water channels, that it is impracticable, if not impossible, to fence it.

For some years Cameron ran flocks of merino sheep in the West Matukituki, driving them out over 50 kilometres down the river for shearing at Wanaka Station.

Around the same time Cameron settled in the valley, Thomas Russell and Joseph Ewing set up the Matukituki timber mills at Mill Creek, on the other side of the river, employing up to a dozen men. Another mill appeared, the Templeton Mill, up the east branch of the Matukituki at Snowy Creek, and a third one near the patch of bush on the bank opposite Wishbone Falls. The conditions were primitive at best. At Mill Creek, or Corner Burn as it was then known in the Scottish parlance, sawmillers and their families lived in wooden cottages surrounded by picket fences and berry bushes. It was in a dark corner of the valley where the forests grew thick, and in the middle of winter the ropes, chains and saws would be covered in hoar frost — with the very ground beneath their feet frozen solid for months on end. Wages were low, but the demand for timber downstream and further east was great, particularly from the gold prospectors.

The millers used a steam engine imported from England to drive the mill and sent long-bearded bushmen into the hills with axes and hand-saws to bring down suitable beech trees. From the mills they floated logs, tied into rafts with flax, down the river to Lake Wanaka. Reports from travellers to the area riding back to Pembroke, Wanaka's name back then, filled readers' heads with awe, particularly those who had travelled up the east branch of the river. One contributor to the *Otago Witness* wrote about the conditions in February 1893:

> People who buy the timber, and probably growl at the price they are asked for it, can have little conception of the hardships and privations the man must face to procure the material for the buyer's convenience. The sawyers here live in a state of banishment, some 30 miles away from the nearest post office; it is safe to say beyond the outskirts of civilization, with no chance of any stray passers-by, and very rare visits from friends.

The same report described what must have been a disturbing environment for immigrants of tamer lands.

> It is the right-hand branch where the scenery assumes its most weird — one might almost say its most horrid — forms. It is here where the avalanches come down from the great southern glacier of Mount Aspiring, which is, however, completely hidden from view by the rocks on all sides, rising in almost perpendicular walls for hundreds of feet. In one spot a huge cauldron has been dug out by the descending masses of ice, and into it are still paid the falling avalanches, descending thousands of feet with a roar and a crash that makes the welkin [sky] tremble and shakes the ground beneath your very feet. In spring, it is said, the uproar is nearly continuous and deafening even at long distances. Through the thunder of the avalanche — more dense than that of an atmospheric storm — through the furious hissing of the water, through the grinding noise of the rocks is heard the sharp, cannonlike reports of cracking and breaking ice. But here the sense of sight is affrightened as well as the sense of hearing the scene presented. The dark grey-blue rocks forming the cauldron rising round it in jagged projections add to the deep gloom that fills the hollow, and reminds one of the 'land of darkness and the shadow of death'.

Mt Aspiring Station homestead in 1960, Matukituki east branch, the site of Hugh Macpherson's old homestead.

In 1879 another Scottish Highlander, Hugh Macpherson, acquired an unknown area of land in the Matukituki east branch, the so-called 'land of darkness'. The Macphersons built a small homestead out of native timber from the sawmill upstream. Here they wintered great periods of isolation on their small grazing area. Their aspirations were not as great as the Camerons across the river, and it was mostly a life of subsistence, modelled on the ways of the Scottish crofter. Hugh ran a few cattle for local butchers and reared some good-quality horses, while Mrs Macpherson sold eggs, milk and baking to the sawmillers — with a reputation for spreading butter on her famous scones with her thumb, as was her Highlander custom.

By 1881 Cameron was grazing 3000 sheep through harsh winter frosts, wading naked through swamps and cutting tracks into scrub and fern to find what little he could for his sheep. It was at about this time when the common European rabbit began to invade the valley. Throughout Otago, between 1877 and 1884, 75 runs were abandoned as a consequence of the rabbit plagues. At the same time, Cameron's flocks were being attacked and killed by kea during the winter snowfalls. His sheep tally in 1884 had dropped to under 2000. The following year Cameron was seen to increase his flock to over 4000, only to fall victim to a severe winter the following year. It was a time of relentless frosts. The snow started falling as early as May, lying on the ground until September, and Cameron lost upwards of 2000 sheep. With this final

The site of the old homestead, now Mt Aspiring Lodge and Tititea Outdoor Education Centre.

cruel hand, Cameron abandoned the station to the rabbits, taking the remainder of his flock south, first to Cattle Flat and eventually to the Mount Burke Peninsula.

In 1891, Russell and Ewing gave up their sawmilling licence, the proximity of suitable trees disappearing too far into the mountains from the river. Hugh Macpherson and his family were alone — that is, except for Colin McLaren, the old bullock driver, who built a small hut for himself two miles downriver; the perfect setting to live the life of a hermit.

The next family to face the loneliness of the valley were the Gaelic-speaking Highlanders Duncan Macpherson, his wife and two children. Duncan was a nephew of Hugh, and had acquired Cameron's Crown runs 458 and 468 in 1899, extending to the top of Mount Aspiring, which they called Mt Aspiring Station. But such was the impact of rabbits that Duncan soon fell behind on his lease payments. To support his family he was forced to leave home for a fortnight at a time to do government road work. Each time he did, he left his wife, four daughters and a son to fend for themselves. They lived in a small homestead near the old mill on the exposed, dark side of the West Matukituki River, opposite Wishbone Falls, beside a tributary now known as Macpherson Creek.

In the summer their lives depended on tending the small garden, hens and ducks, foraging for berries around the old mills, and living off rabbits and the odd mutton carcass. Inevitably, they faced tremendous hardships. The main consideration for many

The rocky terraces above the Matukituki River, near the site of Duncan Macpherson's homestead.

of the early homesteads in these valleys was access to water and firewood, but it wasn't long before they found out about the violence of the valley's north-west winds, and in the winter the sun appeared on this part of the valley for just two and a half hours a day. One of their children eventually drowned in a creek near the homestead, slipping, then washed away after chasing her partially deaf father who was departing on one of his excursions. For Mrs Macpherson, the rivers and creeks thereafter became things of abject fear and dread — she would remain isolated by their confines for years on end, always praying for the safe return of her husband.

On 16 July 1902, the *Otago Witness* reported another fatal drowning in the Matukituki River, this time Duncan's uncle up the valley, Hugh. His dray was found capsized in the river, the 'shaft horse' drowned, hopelessly tangled in chains, and the 'leading horse' up to his belly in water, where it had been standing for six hours overnight, its legs swollen and stiff. The inquest revealed Macpherson had been carrying a bottle of whisky, from which a small amount had been taken. What's more, his boots had been removed and discarded. The consensus back in Pembroke was that Macpherson, no stranger to the bottle, had gone to sleep in the back of the carriage, the two old horses plodding through the night as they were accustomed to doing — they knew every step of the way, but then the whole lot toppled over the steep edge of a washed-out bank. Mrs Macpherson, now widowed and in her late sixties, remained at the homestead for some years before she abandoned it, dying not long after and leaving no descendants. Duncan Macpherson and his family continued to live in the valley, a frugal existence that characterized their Highland heritage.

‘Things I saw’

For years the Matukituki Valley remained a little-known corner of New Zealand. Visitors to the valley in the Macphersons’ time were few, but one that did come, English traveller Miss Maud Moreland, published what she saw on her return to England in 1910. The circumstances around the trip are largely mysterious: ‘There is no story — only impressions, gathered in those wanderings: things I saw, things I heard, in isolated settlements, where the men and women, living face to face with Nature, seem to show a readier kindness; where the robuster virtues still thrive.’ Moreland and her travelling companion made two visits; on the second, she explored the Matukituki Valley, first visiting Duncan Macpherson and his family, then staying with her companion at Hugh Macpherson’s abandoned homestead.

Jerry Aspinall’s Mt Aspiring Station homestead on the east branch, previously the site of Hugh Macpherson’s homestead before he drowned in the Matukituki, and then Duncan Macpherson’s homestead, before he abandoned it after the drowning of his wife.

The lower reaches of the West Matukituki.

'It was a forbidding, desolate place', wrote Moreland.

> Great bare mountains ran up in rocky pinnacles and serrated edges on either side. The bush, along the base, had been swept by some forest fire, leaving only a few scattered groups of beech. ... The ground, too, was stony and barren, and cut up by torrents that tear their way from the mountains; and in many places tumbled boulders and tree-trunks gave us plenty to do to get the horses over. It was better in the river-bed, and we rode them through a ford breast deep, and continued along a shingle-spit for a time; and then we saw signs of cultivation — tiny enclosures of starved oats and hay, a potato patch, and then a bit of road, leading past an old byre and a yard, to a little cottage on a green slope. It might, indeed, have been a Highland crofter's home — only built of boards instead of stone. A room had been added as it was wanted to the end,

> but the original dwelling, with its little green porch and window to one side, was just as when Mr. Macpherson built it for his wife; and here they have lived for nine years, and the children know no other home. A path led up to the door through a plot enclosed by a rude fence, and a few flowers showed an attempt at a garden; and a little higher up the hill was another enclosure with currants and gooseberries. Dismounting, I went up to the door and knocked. Great was the astonishment of the lady who opened to me! A visitor was so rare an event that the four children flocked round, staring with all their eyes, but my welcome was of the heartiest. Mrs. Macpherson seized my hand and drew me forcibly into the room, as though she thought I might vanish if she did not hold me fast.
>
> Mrs. Macpherson explained to me she was growing deaf, and 'Macpherson' was worse. 'It's the roaring of the creeks,' she said; 'sometimes I think I'll go mad, and I know I'm going deaf. I've stood there by the door on a spring morning when the snows are melting, and I've counted forty waterfalls, and the roar of them and the roar of the avalanches is enough to send a woman out of her mind! And then, it is that lonely, too — Oh, you don't know what it is to see another face up here besides your children's! It's sometimes eighteen months, and once it was two full years, before I saw the face of a living woman; you must come and see me whenever you can.'

At the end of 1919 the cruel river Duncan's wife had so feared finally claimed her life. She had travelled to Pembroke in a horse and trap to place a vote in New Zealand's twentieth general election, the ninth since women won the right to vote, the first in which women had the right to stand for parliament. It was December, a torrid time to be crossing the Matukituki, with the ice and snow melting rapidly. In sight of the homestead, with Duncan looking on, Mrs Macpherson's gig overturned and she was swept away. The tragedy marked the end of the Macphersons' time in the Matukituki. Falling rapidly into decline and mostly abandoned, the lease was sold by the Crown to Jack Aspinall of Preston, Lancashire.

The east branch of Mt Aspiring Station.

The rain gauge at the homestead.
Opposite: The ford at Glenfinnan Stream.

God willing, weather permitting

Many have commented on the wilderness of the Matukituki, none more prominent than the poet James K Baxter, who penned 'Poem in the Matukituki Valley' on a 1949 documentary trip with artist John Drawbridge, cinematographer Brian Brake and composer Douglas Lilburn. The trip was blighted by terrible weather, and the documentary film about mountaineering, *Aspiring*, was never completed. But from his notes evolved one of Baxter's early poems, which came to mythologize the drama of the valley for generations. Baxter wrote of 'deathly summits', 'waterfalls flinging arrows on their path', 'wading the swollen Matukituki waist-high in snow water', 'stumbling where the mountains throw their dice, of boulders huge as houses', 'the altar cloth of snow', and an 'avalanche that shook the rough moraine with giant laughter'. All those who enter the Matukituki Valley, even those who have been there countless times before, can't help but be struck by its moods, for the land is ever-changing, and there are many forces hard at work.

Forty-five million years ago the Southern Alps began to rise from the earth's crust, and each year they continue their journey upwards from the fault lines and collisions of the Australian and Pacific tectonic plates at a rate of over 10 millimetres per year. From the mountains were formed great tentacles of ice that carved out grand valleys and then retreated, leaving rivers in their place. The spear-headed peaks that predominate the ranges of west Otago, the 'Otago Alps' as they are sometimes known, are a result of this glacial regime, as opposed to the folded block mountains of central and eastern Otago. For much of the last two million years the Matukituki Valley lay buried under glaciers up to 1000 metres thick, gradually sculpting its U-shaped formation, leaving a landscape of shorn rock and debris.

With its place well back in the mountains the station is subject to unpredictable weather at any time of the year. New Zealand is a 'roaring forties' country, and its weather systems generally prevail in a west-to-east pattern. With no landmass in their path, by the time the currents of the Southern Ocean hit the coast of New Zealand they've built up a considerable head of steam. At Mt Aspiring Station the all too familiar sight of hogsback clouds, with their distinctive lens-shaped tops, indicate gales above the peaks, and usually signal the advance of a real trembler. After a few light gusts the sand will flick up on the riverbeds upstream, followed by a fearsome roaring sound as the wind spills down through the bushclad gorges. Over the years the Aspinalls have seen their fair share of destructive winds and endured countless sleepless nights, wondering if anything would be left in the morning. As a young man in the early 1940s, not long after his father Jack died leaving Jerry and his mother Amy

In the eastern rain shadow of the Southern Alps.

to run the station, Jerry witnessed the garage disintegrating, a sheet of corrugated iron wrapped around a fence post. As he battled out of his truck to check the damage, a gust of wind blew the vehicle, with the brakes on, 200 yards up the flat. Further up the road he met bits of the woolshed flying down the valley. 'On arrival home there was no woolshed, no sheep and shearing suspended until we could collect up enough pieces to build a shelter to work in. What a wind that was.'

In the early days on the other side of the river, before the shelter belts had matured, the homestead would shake, clothes would thrash about on the line, the out-house would be thrown sideways, and buckets and dog kennels blown into the hills. By the river, clouds of dust, stones and sticks would thrash down the valley, and where the two valleys met, east and west branch, whirlwinds would sweep the debris hundreds of feet into the sky.

As the weather systems from the West Coast hit the Alps they rise up, cool down, and release moisture as rain and snow. Snow and ice is a perennial sight on the peaks above the station and it will fall on most of the high slopes for eight months in a year, but it can also throw a dense white blanket over the home paddocks. One year it lay

The snow-fed waters of the Matukituki River at its confluence with Lake Wanaka. Left: A hoar frost around the homestead at Mt Aspiring Station, 1968.

on the ground in front of the homestead for 70 days, and when there was bad weather like that, the Aspinalls prayed the store cupboards were full because it wasn't worth leaving. Snow can arrive on the paddocks as early as May, but often the most severe dumps come in July and August. When it gets up to the 10-inch mark it can create havoc in the forests, something Jerry remembered vividly, for as long as he lived: 'On occasions I have listened, day and night, to continual cracking, almost like intermittent rifle fire, as large branches, unable to carry any more weight, break off and fall to the ground.'

The warm summers are typical of the Otago Lakes region, but winter draws breath early in the Matukituki, and frosts can occur at any time. In the autumn long translucent icicles begin to form on bluffs and around waterfalls as the temperature plummets. And in June and July the frosts begin to thicken. If there's enough vapour in the surface air a freezing layer of fog will develop, enveloping anything exposed to the night air with a milky white rime ice, known as a hoar frost. In places the ground remains frozen all winter. This was especially noticeable on the dark side of the valley, where the Macphersons built the old homestead. They had about four hours of sunshine a day — on a good day — from about 10 o'clock in the morning till two in the afternoon, and by three, the puddles had begun to freeze over again.

Conversely, in the spring and autumn, the freeze and thaw actions left the ground soggy and damp through eight inches of soil, wearing out shoes in a matter of weeks. Willie Aspinall,

Autumn icicles form beneath a bluff in the Matukituki.
Right: A frozen stream near the old homestead, 1968.

Hells Gate, the ice-shorn cliffs that mark the entrance to the West Matukituki Valley.

Sue Aspinall.

Jerry and Phyllis's second son, grew up at the homestead across the river, and was used to the daily tasks of living with the ice. 'The pipes in the toilet and the bathroom used to freeze quite regularly,' he recalls. 'When we were kids one of our jobs used to be to disconnect all the pipes and pull all the drain bungs out so that the pipes and drain wouldn't freeze and split. On occasion we did get caught out and some of them froze up, but we had spirit blow-torches and we would go and thaw them out again. Another job we had as young kids, if the pipes had burst, was to fill up an old tin bath with ice from the creek and drag it back in as we had a copper and could thaw the ice down to use in the homestead. No such thing as ringing up a plumber.'

Vehicles were affected, too. 'There was no antifreeze back then either, so if we wanted to use a vehicle we had to fill it up with water, then drain it out again when we were finished to stop the radiators cracking.' Drying clothes in the damp homestead was a cause of constant agony for Phyllis and Amy Aspinall, and on clear mornings they might not have received any respite outside either, as clothes would freeze solid within minutes of hanging them on the line.

Snow and ice can cause havoc at Aspiring, especially if it comes early in the season, but it's the rain that is the perennial factor. Down by the river the sandflies are said to swarm just before a 'big rain'. But weather changes are often drastic, with little warning. Rainfall varies wildly up and down the length of the Matukituki. The average is 2000 millimetres per year at the homestead, and at the top end of the station, near Aspiring Hut, it's generally 100 per cent more, 4000 millimetres, while 59 kilometres down the road from Aspiring Hut in Wanaka it's just 680 millimetres, half the national average. The station sees around 141 rain days per year, and the heaviest deluges come from the north-west, often in October and November during the lambing period. In November 1957 there were 27 wet days followed by 25 more in December, and in 1988 the station recorded 685 millimetres of rain over a 28-day period in October, with up to a metre and a half at the top end of the station.

On days when the weather prevented work on the hills — 'blue duck days' they'd sometimes call them — the rain unrelenting, the fog too dense, the ground sodden and unstable, John Aspinall wouldn't be far from the road. Whatever he was doing, maybe an odd job he'd been putting off since the spring, or repairing a bit of washed-out fenceline, he was never too busy to talk about the weather with passers-by. And while John was out talking about the unreliability of long-term forecasting, Sue was at the homestead taking weather readings every morning, a tradition started by Amy Aspinall in the 1920s.

Christopher Aspinall.

The station is the first to know about the storms billowing out from the Alps, and it always played an important role in warning the others down the valley about what was heading their way. Amy Aspinall was famous for always finishing off conversations with staff and contractors in her thick Liverpudlian accent: 'DVWP, *Deo volente*, God willing, weather permitting.' The responsibilities of daily weather recording were also occasionally left to the children of Aspiring, who grew up learning which mountains to look over to see where the weather was coming from. 'You always looked over to Aeroplane Peak,' John and Sue's daughter Catie would remember. 'A lot of the weather would come from the west, and if on a nice clear day you started to see some wispy clouds around the top of Aeroplane then you'd start to think there was probably going to be a change. Often it would be a big rain, and soon, sure enough, you would see the clouds rolling in from that direction.'

Wind direction was important, too. 'Then you'd sometimes be looking to see which direction the wind was coming from, and you often knew if it was coming from the south it was going to be cold, and if it was after rain you knew it was probably going to clear over the next few days. We had to record the rainfall every morning from the rain gauge in the garden, record the temperature and then work out how much the trees were being blown about and write it along the bottom. Each month they were sent away to MetService, but if the weather was bad you'd often get phone calls from

different stations down the valley because if there was going to be a big rainfall we would get it first.'

When a big rain does set in, it's not long before the animals retreat to high ground, as dozens of streams boil out across the flats and hundreds of waterfalls leap off the bluffs. 'The noise of them is amazing,' Christopher Aspinall says. 'You just can't help but hear it. Especially at the old homestead. My mother reckoned she could count 52 waterfalls from the kitchen window, and of course there was only one creek, so there was just water everywhere. It might rain for a week without stopping, and the river could turn into a raging flood in a matter of hours.'

The Matukituki River is 30 kilometres long, from the confluence of its west and east branches at the haybarns of Cameron Flat to its meeting place with Lake Wanaka. In the late summer months the Matukituki River will provide glimpses of paradise — crystal clear pools with rainbow trout nestled alongside little silver-grey beaches. But there's a clue to the river's temperamental nature in the Maori meaning of the name: 'pounding stream'.

In the spring and early summer the river levels fluctuate from day to day due to changeable weather and the prevailing warm north-west winds that have a significant effect on the rate of thaw. As a result, it's often in the 'dry' months that the Matukituki can be at its most fierce. Because of its source, the glacial mountains around Mount Aspiring, the river also carries a lot of rock flour, fine silt generated by glacial erosion on the underlying rocks. Its course then is forever changing, and its floor is often softer than a possum's belly.

The river was what prompted Jerry and Phyllis Aspinall to build a new homestead in 1969 on the opposite side. Built of Oamaru stone and Decramastic tiles, the homestead sits on a terrace between two streams, the Niger and Glenfinnan. There are still a number of streams to ford between here and the end of the station, and in the opposite direction back to Wanaka. Some of these have now been bridged, but in John Aspinall's time station vehicles would always carry a tow-rope and a can of CRC, finding that a lot of visitors would still try to rush the remaining creek crossings. It was commonplace to be pulling at least one vehicle out per week, but cars running out of petrol, skidding into fences or getting stuck in the mud have always been a problem on these back country roads.

In Jack Aspinall's time the journey to Wanaka was arduous all year round — in the summer the rivers roared to life with the thaw, and in the winter, although the freeze could lock up most of the moisture in ice, what tracks there were regularly turned to

Clockwise from top left: One of the many waterfalls that form in the Matukituki when the snow begins to melt [*Image courtesy of Kieran Scott*]; a narrow gorge strewn with boulders in the West Matukituki [*Image courtesy of Kieran Scott*]; long icicles hanging beside the Mount Aspiring road; the braids of the Matukituki River [*Image courtesy of Kieran Scott*]; rapids fed by melting ice and snow [*Image courtesy of Kieran Scott*].

'Cattleyards' paddock.

mud. A huge improvement came in 1939 when the Ministry of Works widened the road around the bluffs at Glenfinnan enough to fit a truck the Aspinalls purchased called the 'Bomber': a Bedford that could get them as far as Cameron Flat. Yet even though two of the three dangerous river crossings were avoided, washouts and slips on the road were commonplace. 'It wasn't unusual to put chains on the old truck and literally plough the last twelve miles home,' Jerry told readers in his book *Farming Under Aspiring*.

The uppermost soils that make up the station flats and terraces were deposited by erosion and glacial outwash. Much of the grazeable country is actually part of the Matukituki flood plains, and over the years the river has taken back laboriously developed roads and pastures with indifference. Even today replacing fences is a constant chore, but Randall is quick to remind himself of the work done by his father and grandfather before him. One of the first spring jobs Jerry Aspinall would undertake each year was tree-planting along the riverbanks. From a large nursery by the homestead up to 1000 trees were planted each year, mainly willows and poplars, the fast-growing roots of which bind the soil together to help stop the river breaching the banks.

Above and next page: Snow on the flats, August 2009. Right: Phyllis Aspinall with John.

There are very few stations in the high country that are split in two by such a capricious river. 'So many family activities were controlled by it,' Phyllis once wrote.

> Though it often looked gentle and serene, one could not assume that, because crossing had been simple in the morning, one just entered at night without first studying the situation. Water levels very often rose during the day, and after a flood caution was necessary in deciding upon a safe crossing. The bed was about a half a mile wide, and you took your courage into your hands when you went into the river — often the creeks too. Sometimes it was fairly shallow and the boys could boulder-hop. The general

pattern was when Jerry got to the riverbank he would make a little stack of stones on the edge of the water. When he came home again he would look at that little stack and if it was at the same altitude he would know it was alright to go across. If it wasn't safe we would sleep on the hay — everyone in the family did that quite a few times.

Over the years there have been many fatalities in the Matukituki River, particularly trampers, even experienced ones, underestimating its speed and depth. On many occasions station hacks, and latterly four-wheel drives, were called on to help unsuspecting visitors over the dirty river. Now there are several footbridges to allow crossing when it's too high to wade. But Jerry Aspinall's advice still rings true for all those visiting the Matukituki Valley: 'Never take risks with a river, especially when it's dirty.'

River-crossing stories

Jerry Aspinall: 'Horses strange to the local conditions seemed to try to walk on the surface of the water and tended to panic when they found they couldn't. For our own safety and to get work done it was essential to have horses that were reliable and could be depended upon to be sure-footed and "feel" their way through deep and dirty water, sensing quicksands, boulders and washouts and able to "breast" the current without panic. Fortunately, we had some very good heavy hacks. Some of our horses were very good at double banking or taking two people at once. It was the people that had to be watched. They would look at the dirty surging water and become giddy, not knowing if the horse was going backwards or forwards or even sideways or stopping altogether. In conditions like this these people were given strict instructions not to look at the water, but to keep their eyes on some object on the far bank so they could tell where vertical was.'

Willie Aspinall: 'Often you couldn't get a vehicle across the river to the road head. I can recall coming back from Wanaka and catching the horses and riding back across the river. Usually Mum would be on one horse and John on the front of her and he would have a box of something, like the mail, then I would be with Dad, hanging on to a box of groceries on the front of the horse, too. If the river was up a bit it was the only way to get home. And if we got back really late we slept in the hay and went across the next morning. It wasn't unusual and to us it wasn't a big deal; it was just life as we knew it. Mum didn't like sleeping in the hay because of the possums, so she would sleep in the car. But the rest of us were quite happy to curl up in the hay and go to sleep in the shed. We usually had a sleeping bag or two, but it didn't matter, you could burrow in, as long as you were out of the wind.'

Sue Aspinall: 'I had huge respect for that river and I still do. I remember a few times getting stuck on boulders in the middle of the river, up near Aspiring Hut, and that really scared me — but I had faith in John and he usually got us out by reversing backwards and forwards. He could read the river so well. I would struggle to read a riverbed, as to where you could safely cross, just from the turbulence and colour. I know that if you can't see the bottom you shouldn't go in because there are areas of quicksand.

'Often you only have to get off the crossing by a few metres and you're in trouble. And I do know now that you cross on the top of a bar, where a river might split into two streams and you get a shallow bit — just before it splits. But I also know the wide, calm-looking water isn't always the best! And further up the valley you go in the river the boulders always seem to be bigger, and it was very difficult to see them or how big they were. One time in particular we got very stuck on top of a rock, so John just worked the Landcruiser until we got off. I used to have to close my eyes — he certainly used to take us places I didn't think he should go. I would start yelling: "Let me out, let me get out!" But he wouldn't let me — he was a wee bit like a Barry Crump sometimes. It was something that you learned from the generation before, and also just trial and error. Sometimes he did get really stuck, even though he had all those years' experience. He would have to come home to get a tractor to pull himself out. If I needed to cross, or John wanted me to take a vehicle over, I was happy to do it if the crossing was stable. If it was a bit dicey I had to go with someone else. But I very seldom felt very confident telling people how to cross the river, or where to cross. I just believe that's something you need to have the experience for.'

Randall Aspinall: 'Mum always made a point of taking us for swimming lessons as soon as we were capable because Dad never knew how to swim. We've always had a

The river crossing at Cameron Flat.

liberal upbringing, and we just sort of knew when the river was no good. I think where a lot of people get into trouble is they just don't understand; someone that doesn't know anything about rivers is more likely to try to cross a flooded river than someone who has been around them all their life. So maybe we always just knew instinctively, and by watching Dad reading the river. Like a lot of high country places there's no instruction manual, it is more of an inbuilt or learned thing through experience. We just grew up knowing it was something you don't mess with. Every time we go out working we usually cross it back and forth once or twice a day. I'm by no means an expert at reading the river but I very rarely get stuck when I'm not in a hurry. When you're in a hurry you sometimes think, "I probably shouldn't do this ..." Fairly often we won't be able to get across. And when you get 150 millimetres of rain you can't even get over Glenfinnan Creek, so you can't shift stock. It's a good chance to catch up on office work and odd jobs!

'The number of creeks also means it's hard to fence. When the creeks are high they'll wash away fences. It's also hard on vehicles being in water all the time. Sometimes if you went through too quick you got water in the distributors. If the old cars broke down it wasn't too hard to fix them, and although they don't break down as often, new cars are computer-driven and they're pretty much impossible to fix on the spot.'

The Matukituki west branch.

The reflection of the Mount Avalanche Glacier in autumn.

The station killing shed.

Opposite: Allison Aspinall's hospital paddock.

A silk purse from a sow's ear

Living as the Aspinalls have, this far back in the valley, everyday life at the homestead has a pattern to it that endures. It also has a set of peculiarities and hardships which each generation has had to adapt to their own way. Grandma Phyllis always said that each generation has it easier than the last, 'and so they should, too', but some days the pressure to do things a certain way, to live up to the expectations of previous generations, knowing what they went through, can play at the front of one's mind.

Even this late in the season, down beneath the homestead by the faded colours of the riverbank willows, the sound of the 'loopies' — outsiders — crackling along the metal road continues all through the morning. After a long night hunting in the garden Grimsby the cat settles into his basket by the old stone fireplace, and while Allison Aspinall's father Richie is out digging for potatoes in the vegetable patch, her mother

From left: Grandma Phyllis Aspinall at her home in Wanaka; Allison's father Richie returning from the vegetable garden.

Bev is in the kitchen preparing yet more roast mutton to feed the hungry horde. The Aspinalls have always operated an open kitchen of sorts up here in the mountains and the shepherds are what they call 'fully found'. Usually, it's just one or two workers, a contractor if they're about and the family themselves. But as people began to take notice of the valley beyond Lake Wanaka it wasn't unusual to feed up to 12 visitors at a time, as rabbiters, trampers, deerstalkers, possumers — anyone within earshot of the kitchen gong — were invited in for a meal at a perfectly set table.

For those marrying into the Aspinall family a constant stream of unexpected visitors at the door has often been the most confronting thing to get used to. When Phyllis arrived by dray in 1950 she soon found out that daily life revolved around this. It was a daunting realization, especially for someone with so little cooking experience. 'Just before we got married, Jerry told me he wanted everyone who came to the door to be offered a cup of tea, and I thought, well, no panic, there wouldn't be all

From left: Fred the sheep; Allison in the Aspiring kitchen; the homestead gong; Allison's mother Bev tending the garden.

that many people. But I didn't really know what I was agreeing to. I never knew when I got up in the morning how many people would be at the kitchen table — there could be 16 men all lined up. They'd come during the night, or since dinner the night before. It was by no means a tidy little arrangement, shall we say. You never knew, when you rang the gong for a meal, who and how many would turn up to eat each time. It was anyone that was within earshot, I suppose, and you had people from all walks of life — you might have had your own ploughman and a professor from university around the dinner table at the same time!'

Amy Aspinall had already set a tough precedent for Phyllis: word of her hospitality had spread throughout the nation's alpine fraternity and, having spent several years as a chef on Cunard liners, Jack also well knew how to make a silk purse from a sow's ear. When climber Paul Powell arrived at the homestead in the summer of 1943 to work during the university holidays, he was struck by both the friendliness with which he was welcomed by Jerry and the gusto with which Amy set about her kitchen affairs. 'I'd seen cheery back country housewives before, but the character of this woman compelled you to watch. At breakfast the next morning the kitchen buzzed as she flew to her work. She piled our plates with meat, kept our cups brimful, stoked the fire and, with a flurry of hands, started her day's baking. All the while she talked and

joked with a crossfire of questions and directions. She must have seen me gawking, for suddenly she paused. "Better shut your mouth, lad, before the flies get in." Her laugh was quick, but I could feel her wondering how much use the new chum would be on a station where there was so much to do, and so few to help. This was the woman who had left the closeness of a large Liverpool family to trek with her husband to the lonely outback of Aspiring in 1920. I saw no sign of self-pity. She was a woman in the prime of her life; Aspiring was her home; she was content.'

It was a different life back then, isolated under the shadow of the avalanche. When the homestead was relocated to the opposite side of the river, beside the public road connecting the growing number of alpine huts up the valley, travel to Wanaka became a lot more frequent. Since then even more of the creek fords have been bridged and, with trees lining most of the roadside banks, slips aren't as common as they once were. Even so, it's still Allison's job to keep the station cupboards full and the staff fed, and these young shepherds have been known to work up insatiable hungers. One of the workers in Sue and John's time managing the station, Jeremy Silva, certainly remembered as much. 'Most of the work we were doing was tough, hard, physical work and we had to be good at everything. As a young growing lad I would go up there weighing about 11 stone and would weigh about nine stone by Christmas. And it wasn't because I wasn't well fed — I was a glutton — and every meal tasted fantastic. You couldn't eat enough; we were embarrassingly hungry. When Sue went to town once, the worker and I cooked a whole pot of spuds and ate the whole lot in one go. We had to lie down on the kitchen floor we were so full.'

The kitchen has always been well stocked, and even today it still takes some planning, and Phyllis would remind both Sue and Allison not to be frivolous. 'I was to be frugal and economical, and use what was growing there instead of buying, if I could,' Phyllis said. 'It's amazing what you can use when you have to. Jerry's mother had been there for thirty years before me, and things had been very hard for her. When she first went it would take three days to do the shopping. They would go down to Wanaka in a dray, five times through the river. It would take them all day to do their shopping and catch up on people. And then the third day to go home again. And it was hours — Jerry used to say he would sleep on the bottom of the dray going up and down. That would be once every quarter that they would go and get more supplies. And they would have to be careful because they couldn't afford very much to start with.'

Julia Aspinall, Phyllis's youngest child, would remember her mother and father taking over from Amy and Jack in much the same way. 'Mum and Dad lived almost a subsistence lifestyle, living off the land, which means a lot of hard work. They recycled everything. They'd recycle Gladwrap, they'd recycle plastic bags ... and they'd grow as many fruit and veges as they could. They'd blanch them and freeze them when they were in season, and they'd do a lot of preserving. I don't think she found any of it very easy. But she made the most of it. She was certainly resourceful, too, and did really long hours. But she didn't take short cuts and she put a lot of effort into cooking to make sure it was done in a tasteful way. But mostly it was mutton — for breakfast, lunch and dinner, and we ate all of the animal, not just bits of it; we had to eat everything on our plate. Dad would eat the liver and kidneys — he used to love offal. "Waste not, want not" — that was my father's favourite saying.'

The Aspinall palates wouldn't tire of the stronger, tougher aged mutton. In Sue's time the mainstay was always mutton, not lamb, even at Christmas. 'In our early times beef was too valuable to kill as house meat and, even so, to this day I just never get sick of mutton. Pork we hardly ever had and in our early married life it was a treat to buy chicken. I would still buy a little bit of chicken for the farm, just because when you're feeding staff it's nice to have variety, even though John and I would have been happy to eat mutton every day.'

The garden was prolific at the old homestead across the river. It contained almost all the fresh produce the Aspinalls ever needed, including raspberries, gooseberries,

Clockwise from top left: Shepherd Struan Mehrtens; Aspen poplar trees below the homestead; shepherd Monique King; Sue Aspinall.

SWAZI

currants, rhubarb, potatoes, peas, carrots, parsnips, beans, Brussels sprouts and turnips, and from a small glasshouse came lettuce, cabbages, cauliflowers, tomatoes, cucumbers and grapes. Even so, the winter was a problem. It was so cold that flower vases full of water would turn to ice on the windowsill, and potatoes had to be kept in straw in the woolshed to stop them freezing solid. It also meant the growing season was short, and to make the most of the garden, preserving was essential. When she first arrived, Phyllis didn't know a thing about cooking and preserving. She started out following some of Amy's recipes, but without her immediate presence she soon turned for help to the Home Science Extension Department's national information service, set up by Emily Elizabeth Carpenter to meet the cooking and housecare needs of rural women in New Zealand.

'I was forever writing to them,' Phyllis recalled. 'Their aim was to teach women properly how to cook and keep house — all sorts of things about cleaning, cooking and laundry. They were a great joy and help. The tutors used to come around at preserving time and give lectures to the Women's Division, telling them how to preserve different things, shall we say. One came especially from England to teach embroidery, basket-making and glove-making. So there was a whole diversity of skills you could learn through them. They never knew what was coming — a whole assortment of strange questions.

'The reason why I decided to try bottling a bullock was because sometimes we ran out of mutton. But he [Jerry] always wanted meat on the table. Chops for breakfast, usually cold meat or stew for lunch, and a hot roast at dinner. And I wasn't ever allowed to buy meat or tins of fish. And if there was no meat, they would say it was too hot to kill, or it would go bad straight away, or it was too wet, or they couldn't get across the river to get a carcass; they would have an excuse of some sort or another, but they still wanted meat on the table. It was a real burden to me.

'In the end I made a handsome discovery. When I read about bottling the beast, it seemed to be the answer. Sometimes if a little young beast, at mustering time, might break a leg they would bring it and set it up on the gallows and hope that it would heal. But it never did, the poor things, and to bring a vet from Dunedin, the nearest place, was too expensive; it would cost more than the animal was worth. So I decided it would be a sensible thing to destroy the beast and bottle it. The men had to butcher it and cut it up into small pieces, and the meat had to be half-cooked, then you bottled it and cooked it in a pressure cooker. You could do five jars at a time, and you had to leave it in the pressure cooker until the cooker got cold. We would get about 90 jars out of just one bullock. Which meant I could do it three times in a day, 15 jars. You left it on the second day, then on the third day you repeated the performance. It was a major effort. There would be two men cutting up little cubes of beef, or mincing, and it took them forever. We'd have steak and kidney, steak and onions, mince and soup. And I bought leeks and celery, which we didn't grow, so that we could have a different flavour for the soup. And to have all the jars was a wonderful comfort, and then to have that food to have to use through the year was a marvellous solace. It made a wealth of difference to my happiness for one thing.'

Two generations on and it remains one of the most fundamental facts of life on an isolated station; nothing goes to waste. Part of Allison's daily routine is to walk past the old killing shed to the hospital paddock each morning with the food scraps. 'Hi, Fred, where's Derek? Then there's Daphne, Mark, Marge, "No-neck" and Scoury … I only give them proper names when I know they're going to live,' says Allison. 'Before that they have reserve names like "X".' Death is something people have to adjust to quickly in the country, and it was always something the Aspinall kids were exposed to on the station from an early age. 'They experience nature on its own terms,' John would say. 'Certainly, bringing them up in an environment like this gives children a good understanding of nature, of its whims, its changes, reproduction of plants, life and death — they accept that animals are born, live their time and die when life is finished.'

Having worked as a physio at the freezing works in Invercargill, Allison was used to seeing slaughtered animals, but somehow it's always different when they're your own. 'When we first moved up it seemed an awful lot of the sheep died,' she recalls. 'I think we just caught a bad patch, but I have also had a pretty bad success rate with my pet lambs. Four out of eight died in the first year and two out of four the second year. I get upset each time, but the longer I'm here the more I come to accept that it's just part of life on a farm. And as Gary the vet always said, if you have live stock, you have dead stock! And when life is finished, on a farm it often means it'll end up on someone's plate, or in a dog's bowl.

'I suppose that's where Catie's comment came in,' remembers Sue. 'Just before my father's funeral she asked, "Mum, is Granddad going to be fed to the dogs?"'

The first tractor operated by the Aspinalls on Mt Aspiring Station.

Fordson

Lambs on Mineral Pool Hill.

Opposite: Allison feeding scraps to her pet sheep.

Life as we knew it

Willie Aspinall: 'Growing up at Aspiring, after life as we knew it, the hard part was going to boarding school. It was a totally, totally different environment, and we had to do things that, for me anyway, I often resented. All of a sudden everything revolved around a clock. You had to be up by a certain time, have your bed made by a certain time, go to school by a certain time. Up until then time didn't really mean anything. I don't think I ever acclimatized.'

Being out with the animals is something Allison Aspinall has grown an affection for in her short time at Mt Aspiring Station — and it is infectious, rearing orphaned lambs and calves, weaning sheep, drafting in the cattle yards, experiencing nature on its own terms, but there are other challenges in these hills that take a bit more getting used to.

'It's easy to start to feel isolated,' warns Catie Aspinall, now living in Ireland. 'You can feel like you're just in your own little world out there, surrounded by men, the workers, climbers and hunters, people just passing through. There weren't always a lot of people that came just to have a gossip. You have to make a real effort to stay connected to the rest of the world and you still have to be OK in your own company for long periods of time. I can remember being left alone, Mum had gone into town,

Willie Aspinall at Lake Wanaka.

The homestead settling tank frozen over, July 2007.

Julia Aspinall.

the boys would be out working, and it would be my job to get lunch ready for them. You were quite conscious you were there just by yourself, but you couldn't let it overwhelm you. You had to be an organized person and you have to have a good amount of common sense as you can't always be calling someone to come and fix things.'

Phyllis Aspinall was known never to go further than she could carry her youngest child, and she never learned to drive. 'I grew up during the war and my father didn't want me to be seen practising driving around the place when so many farmers were desperate for petrol. It was still rationed when we got married. And if you saw our road … Sometimes we were stuck all day. There was no telephone, so if I'd been by myself starting from Aspiring nobody would know if I'd even set forth when I didn't turn up!'

Allison Aspinall checking the homestead switchboard.
Below: The pipeline from Glenfinnan Hill.

Today Allison wouldn't think twice about driving herself to Wanaka if she really needed to and, while it's unlikely the valley will ever be within cellphone coverage, it was only 40 years ago that Jerry and Phyllis worked the same property with virtually no telecommunications at all. It was one of the things that most bothered Phyllis when she arrived. Initially, they had radio contact with Dunedin twice a week at eight in the evening, but eventually a radio was installed at Phyllis's parents' house in Wanaka. Every evening at 7 p.m. they could leave messages to be relayed on, but it was reserved for farm matters only — mostly parts for broken-down machinery, or large grocery orders to be brought up by travellers. Although, if the roads were in bad shape, they were allowed to leave messages saying they were coming in, and 'Would they please send out a search party if they were not in Wanaka by a certain time. But no chatter at all,' recalled Phyllis. 'P&T department listened in from time to time, so you weren't allowed to talk trivia.'

Communication with the outside world has improved markedly for the back country stations of Otago over the years, but there are still things to make life challenging, as Allison has come to find. 'The hardest part of adjusting to life here has been getting used to the power and the water. It's quite an antiquated system — basically just a pipe in a creek, so if it rains it'll block up, and then next thing you know there are cattle slopping around in it. It blocks up all the time, so I won't have any water in the house. In town you just turn everything on and it goes, so it's taken quite a bit of time to adjust to.'

Turning the clock back, when the Aspinalls lived on the other side of the river, life was governed by the condition of the wood supply for cooking. 'I cooked on a wood range and the wood was always wet, so you could only cook things slowly. I would control the temperatures by guess and by God, I suppose! You just had to learn these things. If the fire was burning well the embers would burn well, but it always affected the type of things you could cook. You could make soup or stew OK, but not pudding.'

In the mid-1930s a windmill was installed on top of a 70-foot metal tower behind the homestead, feeding a set of 32-volt batteries. There was a petrol engine that had to be hand-cranked into life which ran things like the washing machine on days when there was no wind in the valley. Or if the wind was too strong, the propeller could be blown to the ground. The system kept the lights on and the radio tuned in, but little else.

In the 1950s Jerry began looking to greater heights. He estimated that the waterfall behind the homestead, 500 feet up, had the potential to generate enough power for all the homestead's needs, but it would be no small feat of ingenuity. Jerry ordered 1500 feet of four-inch steel pipe from America, which he carted to the foot of the hill below the falls. From there it was lifted up the slopes with a homemade winch, which Jerry calculated he had turned at least 125,000 times. One of the top-dressing pilots, Tex Smith, was then called on to fly Jerry over Homestead Peak to drop bags of cement near the waterfall. 'I thought the first bag was going straight down the waterfall, but no, a miss by thirty yards,' Jerry later said. 'After five more similar "runs" the rest were on target, no more than five yards apart. There was only a small hole in the turf, and the paper bags shattered, but the contents were safe.'

Later, a group of Alpine Club friends helped Jerry screw the 21-foot lengths together. They were only too willing to help, a small thank you for years of Aspinall hospitality. A small dam and grated intake were blasted out and concreted into the rocky sides of the creek above the main falls, the pipeline was anchored, a building for the generator erected, and soon enough water was coursing through the pipes to run the lights, washing machine, ranges and shearing machines. There was also a continuous supply of hot water, but there were no regulators and the water often boiled over at night, like the sound of a 'hundred opossums gambolling on the roof'. 'We didn't mind, but visitors found it rather disturbing,' said Jerry.

Ever since the hydro-power intake was put in on Mt Aspiring Station the cook had to keep one eye on the scones, one eye on the children and both on the switchboard, but it wasn't such a millstone; they had heaters in the bedrooms, appliances they never thought existed — cake-mixers, electric irons and one of the greatest assets of all for Phyllis Aspinall: a dishwasher. They couldn't use the power enough and, ironically, without a means of storing it, they soon found they ran out of ways to use it. It wasn't uncommon in the summer to see a heater turned up on the front porch as an outlet for the surplus electricity.

Allison with her black-and-white steer Herb, and red-and-white heifer Honey, with two, as yet unnamed, calves.

When the Aspinalls moved across the river, the power plant went with them, erected high up on Niger Stream, directly above the homestead. It remains there to this day, powering the house, workers' quarters and the three-stand shearing shed. Sue Aspinall arrived at Aspiring not long after the new house was built, inheriting the role of supply warden. 'The power took a while to get used to. When I first went there the power plant was having some teething problems. The switchboard used to go "clickety-clack, clickety-clack". You had to use every bit of electricity being generated, and if you didn't it became spare power and went into underfloor heating cables. What made the noise was the process of switching from one thing to another. Then they put in automatic regulators and a switchboard, which cut out all that noise. I just learned to watch the amp meter and volt meter all the time in the kitchen. You learned to tell if it was going off, or if it was stable. If the volts and amps dropped away quickly you could tell what the problem might be. For example, you couldn't have all three hot water cylinders on at once as well as the dishwasher or the oven, and you couldn't boil the jug and have all three shearing machines going together, which I know from experience!

'You soon learn what works and what doesn't. On windy days leaves can block the intake and in the winter it can still switch off if ice forms over the grille, which is no fun at all. In frosty weather we would sometimes take the grille off the intake, but this was a bit of a risk — you would have to really watch the weather because stones could get sucked down the pipe which would cause real problems. Lumps of ice might also form down the pipe and block it. You would always just have to wait until the sun arrived to warm it up.

'In John's parents' day, as the nights got colder it would take longer to clear the ice each morning, so it might be 11 a.m. before you got the power going. Then the sun was gone again by three-thirty in the afternoon, and sun might be off the intake by two, so the power might've only been on for a few hours each day. I was always told not to turn the power on if the temperature was at zero or lower because that could cause a split in the pipe. You just had to cope. Up until Rachal was born I just had one open fire by the living room — then we put in a log burner which you could cook on. But if it was night-time and the power was off you used a gas cooker and candles to see. I didn't enjoy it, but it was part of living at Aspiring and you just had to live with it. John used to say it was character-building, and I used to tell him I had run out of character. I can't tell you how many times I ran out!'

In the kitchen at the homestead there is a cast-iron Atlas heat-storage range, the linchpin of high country cooking in the valley for generations. The stove and cooker store heat from the electricity supply so it can be used throughout the day. There were two of the ranges here originally — their ability to absorb and accumulate a constant heat was a blessing, especially during shearing. Each offered a different amount of heat, one doing the meat and the other the scones, and it was quite commonplace to see one child perched on each warm lid. Today the Aspinalls use most of the unused electricity as underfloor heating, and they have installed air elements on the side of the house that suck out the excess power over the hot summer months.

When Jack and Amy settled at Mount Aspiring in 1920 education was still a real problem in the back country. Many children grew up in the valleys and foothills of the Alps completely illiterate. But in 1922 the Correspondence School was established to provide lessons for the isolated families scattered throughout New Zealand. Every child born at Aspiring has been schooled this way until old enough to attend boarding school, under the watchful eye of a mother — Amy, Phyllis and then Sue. It seemed to work well for the kids: 'Where else can you do correspondence school in the morning, farming in the afternoon, go up the river and catch a fish, then head into the bush and shoot a deer, and be back home and in bed by dark?' John once said.

Sue tried all sorts of tricks to make their education as school-like as she could. 'I found you had to be a bit bloody-minded,' she recalled. 'I tried several different times for starting school lessons, but in the end it was best to start at 8 a.m., when the men went out to work. The kids could have morning tea, but the only break they really had was if I got distracted by answering the phone. Then they were just normal children and took the opportunity to run outside, have a fight or generally do something other than what they were supposed to be doing! We had to have three classes going at the same time — I did that for 14 years, starting when Catie was three, doing pre-school correspondence, and I finished with Rachal's Form Two. I used to tell the kids that they had to be both the teacher and the pupil. So I guess I tried to prepare the kids as much as I could — and I've been told by teachers that they all had pretty good work habits. It's very difficult trying to be mother and a teacher. While I never sat right beside them, I was always in the same room as them. I might at the same time have been preserving fruit, making lunch or carrying on with normal activities, but always with an eye on what they were doing.

'We were allowed to ring the Correspondence School when we liked, in Wellington. They sent out a green canvas bag with lessons set out for 10 school days, labelled by day. At the end of day 10 the book would be bagged up and sent back to Wellington. They would get their workbook back with comments, stars and ticks. The children were all encouraged to write to the teacher, telling them about what they were doing and they built up a terrific rapport. Some of them still ring me to this day.'

Allison, Bev and Monique at the Mount Aspiring homestead.

The kids were also known to use their imaginations to make it seem like any other school. They would make their bed, brush their teeth, get their books ready in their backpacks, say, 'Goodbye, Mum,' walk down the drive, out the gate to the road, and then walk back again, through the kitchen door at 8 a.m. sharp with a beaming smile, 'Good morning, Mrs Aspinall.' But some days, especially at docking time, the kids would have to pack their bags and head out with their lesson plans, sitting under an umbrella or in the back of the car if it was raining, as it often is in the Matukituki Valley.

Does home-schooling change your perspective? 'I don't think so,' says Sue. 'For some it takes longer to get used to working with others. When John was schooled they lived across the river in the East Matuki so they didn't have a lot of interaction with other kids, and when it came time for them to go to boarding school it was quite a shock. When my kids were schooled I made the decision to make that transition easier. So I arranged for our kids to go to Wanaka Primary for one day a week, in a normal class. I think it helped them a lot — I did it purely for social interaction, not for academic reasons.'

When the time came it was never going to be an easy transition, going from the wilds and isolation of the Matukituki to a secondary boarding school in the city. Phyllis's kids were embarrassed at not being able to ride a bike, even though they could all drive a tractor. It seemed to affect two of the siblings in the family in particular: Willie and Julia.

'It was a totally different environment,' remembers Willie. 'John got the hang of it pretty quick. Maybe he was just a bit more adaptable. One thing he told me was that you're meant to call everyone "sir", even though not a single one of them could even dag a sheep. In our view you didn't respect someone because they were a teacher, you respected them for what they could do. I remember having to explain to the teachers why I didn't know what an exam was; they were shocked. Although, there were some other kids like us. Some of them hadn't worn shoes by the time they came to boarding school. One guy unpacked the bag his mother had given him and he said, "What the hell are these things?" — they were underpants, but he had never worn them. I was quite homesick at school for a long time. Often I would go for a run right out to Mosgiel. Three miles there and back again, just to get out of the city. Some things we did learn at Aspiring that we could bring to the school. All of us were in the school shooting team at one stage. But then there were things like school dances — I never did go to a school formal. It was easier to take the punishment. They always encouraged pupils to go on to university, but I'd had enough of it. Straight after school I had a job in Marlborough about as far away from civilization as I could get. I guess it was just what I was used to.'

Julia Aspinall had similar difficulties adjusting to the new regime. 'Boarding school was a major culture shock and I never got used to it. I was there for five years and hated every minute. Suddenly, I seemed to be in a prison ruled by bells. In the morning there was a bell to get up, to start work, to stop work, to take a mid-morning break, to start after the break and to take lunch. The succession of bells continued until we went to bed. We all had uniforms and we had to wear them in a certain way. We all had to go to church on Sunday with our hats, gloves and jackets — everything had to be perfect and we had to be inspected before we went. Pretty horrific it was. I also went from having all brothers to an all-girls environment. And girls are catty, man alive, they're nasty! Part of it was that you weren't really considered to be a person. It's like they thought we were cattle to be whipped into shape.

'Until then school for us had been a bit like a dreamworld, the four of us sitting at our little school desks. There used to be the odd person passing by and Mum and Dad would rake them in, both being very sociable people. But us kids didn't necessarily respond too well to that. John and Christopher were OK, quite sociable, but Willie and I weren't. He would go bush and I would hide under my bed. Then, instead of having our secure little world and our 26,000-acre playground around us, we were suddenly surrounded by all these strangers. You always felt like getting away by yourself for a while, but there was just nowhere to go. As a shy back country girl, I took the loss of freedom hard.'

Although the Aspiring children missed their freedom, they had been instilled with an exceptional work ethic, ploughing through their lessons so they could be out on the farm, where the clock suddenly didn't mean anything any more.

Stock tracks leading to the cattleyards paddock past a haybarn at Cameron Flat.

The West Matukituki, with the familiar sight of Sharks Tooth Peak in the distance.

The woolshed paddock.

A wool broom above a chute at the Mt Aspiring Station woolshed.

Opposite: Baled first crutchings.

Marrowbone country

Nowhere in the world are sheep run across such rugged country in such vast numbers as the high country stations of the South Island. Their 'paddocks' are usually high up in the mountains and, as a result, the soils have low fertility and a short growth period. To compensate, they cover huge areas. The average stocking rate for high country farms is between two and seven stock units per hectare, compared with the North's hill country average of between six and ten. There are fewer fences than low-lying farms, which means a lot of sheep scattered about the slopes for miles in any direction, and it's not until they're gathered on the flats that the size of a high country mob becomes clear. It has always taken a skilled musterer, some well-disciplined dogs or some good improvisation to round them up. And despite the obvious technological developments in high country farming in the last 50 years, notably helicopters, there's still a sense of timelessness to the art of the hill-muster.

On a frosty morning in the Matukituki Valley Randall Aspinall's Landcruiser is warming up in the driveway, clouds billowing from the tailpipe as the windows thaw and the dogs are let loose from the kennels. The forecast is for perfect mustering weather; there's not a cloud to be seen about the tip of Aeroplane. Today Randall, Struan and Monique are mustering the mob of 3000 ewes from their halfway block on the hills near Raspberry Hut, from where they will drive them along the banks of the West Matukituki to the terrace country on the opposite side. There are a few odd fencing jobs to do later in the afternoon, a perennial country task, but mustering above the winter snow line by foot will take up most of the day.

Station hacks are only a distant memory for Randall. The last one died when he was 10 years old, 'a nasty old bastard', and four-wheeled vehicles have long since replaced them. It was a welcome sight for Jerry: 'A machine needs to be carefully looked after, but it doesn't have to be fed when not in use,' and, most reassuringly, 'it's always where you leave it'. Today you can drive down the public road through the middle of Mt Aspiring Station to the Raspberry Hut car park — where the tourists leave their cars — and from here the private four-wheel drive track continues on to Aspiring Hut and the national park boundary. But everywhere else up the west branch you'll have to use your own two feet. And this is seriously steep country, too steep for horses or quad-bikes. There's an old name for it in the South Island, 'marrowbone country', the kind of stuff that brings you to your knees.

Almost everyone has had a close call mustering at altitude. Maybe they've slipped down the hill only to be saved by a tussock, luck on their side. For Struan it's the steeper country he enjoys most about working at Aspiring. Struan is from a farm in the

Ewes crossing the river to the terraced country.

foothills of Springfield in Canterbury, but the challenge of Aspiring's mountains is more than a novelty. 'It's a good playground. Bit more fun and a bit more challenging than other places — she's pretty steep country.' And with Struan's first rugby colts game of the season in a week's time it's also some of the best pre-season heartland training going.

For others it's the hardest thing to adjust to, something Sue Aspinall never quite came to terms with. 'I'm not particularly good with heights,' she says. 'There are some hills I still can't climb; they're just too steep. I would always get down on my backside, or crawl along on my hands and knees, but John soon told me, "That's no way to get up and down a hill! You've got two feet, get up and use 'em!" I was far more cautious. I'm OK if there's a big four-wheel drive track to walk up, but what I'm not good at is walking up what I call a goat track, which is only a few inches wide. That's my biggest challenge, to overcome that fear. Some days it works and sometimes it doesn't. I just freeze and get to a point where I can't go on any more.' But for the Aspinall kids it was just second nature, and John was a great believer in the benefits of walking from the bottom. 'Because, and I agree, you know on the way up what the lay of the land is. It's quite bluffy up there, and there have been accidents where people have fallen off bluffs. John always said that's the one fault of helicopters.'

With a cool breeze snapping about the boulders beneath Craigroyston and Sharks Tooth peaks, Struan sets off on his own two feet, 'hoofing it' with his dogs to muster the ewes from the east. Over the years this type of musterer has been called all sorts of names: scree-scrambler, tussock-jumper, gully-raker — at college John Aspinall was known simply as Mountain Goat — but since the first men and women of the back country arrived here nothing much has changed in the art of mustering these ridges and bluffs. There's no instruction manual for the job of bringing them in — it comes through watching and experience, passed down through generations of growing up in the hills.

Over the years shepherds would turn up in the valley with varying degrees of ability. Generally, they were keen as anything to learn, which in time made all the difference. If they were uneasy they'd be given more junior beats until they became fitter and developed that sixth sense for reading the land. You won't see RM Williams boots up here; you'll need a sound pair of heavy mountaineering boots with good shock absorption, and a pair of long woolly socks. It also helps to have a good level of fitness, or have a team of very good dogs. Fortunately, Struan has both.

Before much of the current fencing was put in on the flats, an area between the river and the top peaks, and 10 kilometres up the valley between Raspberry and Aspiring huts, had to be mustered in one swoop. The muster would take two days, and to make sure they could set off at first light on the second day John and two workers would stay overnight at Cascade Hut. In the summer the sheep would go as high as the scree slopes and, on the odd occasion, the sheep would move right over the top of the Shotover Saddle and down into Branches Station.

Like his father before him, Jeremy Silva worked on the station for a number of years with his brothers, and was one of John's first employees. The Silva family spent 21 Christmases at Raspberry Hut, and some of their first memories as young kids growing up are of helping Jerry with the haymaking. But it was events like the pre-shearing muster the Silva boys remember most of all. 'John was such an awesome character that our job as town boys was to try to impress him, so we used to take all the hard jobs we could. He was very fit and very strong — a powerful brute of a man, and following him up the hill was a mission on its own. He was a front-row forward for Upper Clutha and also the school 1500-metre champion at Otago Boys'. So on the pre-shearing muster I would always take the top beat as a matter of pride, right up into the scree. On the middle beat the person above you would always be pushing stock down, but on the top beat you could easily walk around a ridge and see a group of sheep 500 to 1000 feet above, so you had to go up and get them.

'By the time I got to working there I had been running around the hills since I was

Clockwise from top left: Zac at Hells Gate; sheep crossing the river; Randall Aspinall radioing instructions to Monique; mixed-age Hereford-Angus cows, free to roam the river flats.

Christopher Aspinall.

eight, so it was just assumed we knew what we were doing, but during table-talk at night you would chat about things that happened to people. You're quite often having to make decisions on that country as to whether you try to skirt, stay at the level you're at, climb your way through a creek, or climb down 400 or 500 feet to a safe place to get through a gully. You're making those decisions all the time: do I go round, do I go higher or do I go lower? It wasn't a nice pass round there and at times there would be bracken up to your head, a real big problem in those days. It would stifle you. The other thing that would really get you was the Spaniard grass, which had spikes on it; not like a tussock, more like a cactus. You'd have to beat your way through it and your legs would get ripped to shreds. But it was all good stuff for a young fella!

'The sheep were pretty clever; Perendales are almost like goats. But occasionally you would get some sheep that would get bluffed to the extent they couldn't get back up. I remember having to shoot one once. I quite often carried a rifle on the top beat in case we saw some tahr or chamois. It was certainly good fun getting paid to carry a rifle. And sometimes you would come across the odd three-fleecer up there like Shrek — one that had avoided the muster. You'd probably never finish a muster in that sort of country without a few stragglers. I didn't have a dog, just a polythene dog, which was just a bit of polythene I used to whack on the ground and whirl around, so it required a lot of fitness. And bringing the sheep down the valley without dogs was quite an effort, all the time running up across the valley to keep them moving. It would keep you very, very fit — so fit that I won the South Island 1500 metres championship at the end of the fourth form, straight out of a stint at Aspiring.'

Struan disappears into the folds of the hills, and Randall and Monique continue down the road to bring in the mob from the west. For Monique, it's a daunting prospect, clambering about these rocky slopes, but she takes to it well, and she's here to learn from the best. Randall patrols the bottom beat with his hill-stick and radio, guiding Monique around bluffs, spotting stragglers hidden in gullies. It used to be, without radios, that each shepherd would have their own beat, and be responsible for all the sheep on that beat. 'Now we can all help each other,' says Randall. 'There are things they can see that I can't, but things I can see they can't.'

As with any kind of mountaineering, coming down is always more difficult than going up. And the moment it gets wet, grass and tussock can become as slippery as ice. Under the watchful eye of experienced hands, there have been very few accidents involving shepherds at Aspiring. It hasn't always been so for dogs. Among countless operations in the Matukituki Valley search and rescue veteran Geoff Wayatt would recall one of the more unusual rescues of his career. From the Aspiring homestead Geoff received a call from John asking for a favour. 'I need your help. My musterer's just lost a dog and I need to get him out.'

'Instead of calling search and rescue, he called me,' said Geoff. 'I had a guy working for me at the time, so I called him up and said, "We've got a job to do for a local farmer." It was his day off, but he said, "OK, sounds interesting." So off we went. The

Feeding out hay on Cattle Face, high above the east branch.

Looking for stragglers in gullies, Monique King on the mustering beat.

dog had been coming around a bluff above Raspberry Hut at speed and got airborne, falling 60 foot down into a gorge, but he was still alive. It had spent five hours down there before I got to it — and it was all over me when I did. So I strapped a pack onto it and, as the helicopter came around with a net underneath it, I threw myself in with the dog on my back. It was a prized dog, so the station hand was very appreciative!'

As Monique keeps a careful eye on her dogs following a narrow goat track, suddenly a ewe topples over a bluff, cascading down to a ledge, unmoving. It'll probably recover, for these Romdales are a hardy breed, but it's still a reminder about the hazards of mustering this kind of country for both stock and the musterer — you've got to be careful not to panic the mob, and keep a tight rein on the dogs. Part of the skill is using all your dogs effectively, the mixture of heading dogs, huntaways and handy dogs. The heading dogs will scour the slopes for stragglers and small groups of sheep, pushing them downhill, the handy dogs will 'slew' mobs in the right direction with enough freedom to pick their own track down, while huntaways will often do as much with a chorus of deep-pitched barks, if they're in earshot. The dogs are given names with one syllable, to make it easy to direct, call back, or swear at, as the case may be.

The mob gathers at the river's edge as the three dog teams rein in the flanks. They squeeze together, reluctant on the shore. But it only takes one ewe to make the first plunge and the instinct to follow the leader kicks in. Usually the Aspinalls wait until the river is low to push them into the east branch, often the case after a frost, picking a narrow or wide, shallow crossing. Some of the weaker ones might need a hand, especially if their fleece gets saturated. Today they can thank Huey for a smooth crossing. 'In winter it gets so cold that the water on their backs turns to frost as they come out the other side,' Struan grins. 'It's gone pretty well today — the river is real low, but usually in this bit it's too swift and we'd have to go where it's a bit calmer. You have to be careful because they might pile in too quickly, and if one falls over at the front the rest will pile over the top and drown it.'

Other times they don't move at all, which, given the nature of the environment, can easily end in tragedy. As Jeremy Silva remembered, those were the moments the Aspinalls dreaded. 'After the hoggets had been in for shearing one year John took them up the valley to try to get them across the river to a block up the east branch. For sheep the river was pretty much like a fence. He spent about eight hours and got them as far as an island in the middle, but couldn't get them to go any further. You sort of had to carry the hoggets into the river and once they were swimming the others would follow, but that day they stayed on a small island and he couldn't get them off. He lost a lot of sheep that night, dead from exposure. The next day all of a sudden two or three of them swam for it and we got them off, but he had already lost 30 or 40 sheep — it was just heartbreaking.'

Wool in the press; shearing combs and cutters.

The fine-woolled merino was the first breed to be imported in great numbers to the New Zealand high country, on the back of the successful Australian example. Marrowbone country didn't lend itself to meat breeds, which had to be effectively fattened on low-lying country. And besides, even after the advent of refrigeration, for generations the main product of the high country was wool. With their strong constitution, mountain-climbing tendency and prized fleeces — thick all year round — merinos quickly became the backbone of the high country economy. When Ewen Cameron arrived in the Matukituki Valley in 1878 he brought with him a flock of these mountain-climbers, but it didn't take him long to realize the merino is at a distinct disadvantage to other breeds in wet conditions. In high-rainfall areas like the Matukituki their overcoats are perpetually damp and prone to fleece rot.

The heavy rainfall, boggy mires and snow-fed streams of the valley caused ruinous problems for Cameron, and it wasn't long before he would favour half-bred Romneys, a sheep with native origins in the wet, low-lying countryside of Kent in England. The Romney was an exceptional dual-purpose breed fit for heavy soils. They were also reasonable climbers, Jerry noticed. But hoping to find an even livelier progeny Jerry experimented with Perendales, a cross between a Romney and a Cheviot. The Perendale had been developed at Massey University by Sir George Peren in the 1950s to be more productive on hill country, with less palatable feed. The Cheviot was originally from the border country between England and Scotland — the Cheviot Hills. It was a tough, dual-purpose mountain breed. The resulting Perendale was very active, a good forager at altitude, moving well across large areas. Lambing percentages at Aspiring would spike up 20 per cent as a result of introducing the Perendale. Later still, the Perendale was crossed with a Romney, to provide more wool and greater carcass size. Today Aspiring's flocks are made up of this 'Romdale' breed, deep-bodied with powerful hind-quarters, a hardy constitution with good fertility rates on unshepherded country.

They produce strong wool at Mt Aspiring Station from their crossbred Romdales. It's a coarse, thick wool: ideal for carpets, knitting yarn, blankets and upholstery, with New Zealand contributing almost a quarter of the world's total. But the disorganization of the wool industry for years now has meant that, for some, wool has become almost a liability, with little profit left behind after the costs of shearing, exporting and marketing. It's still a worthwhile by-product at Aspiring and necessary for the animals' welfare, but the focus is prime lamb production and, as a result, spring is always a tense time in this fickle alpine environment. The flock of 5000 sheep the Aspinalls run at Mt Aspiring Station is about the same as Ewen Cameron had in the nineteenth century. But in Cameron's day flock mortality rates were high and most lambing was for replacement. Fencing and the ability to control stock is one of the big differences. The ability to fence off sunny faces for winter grazing, hold stock off particular areas, prevent them going too high, and contain them during the mating season has significantly increased lambing percentages. It also helps to isolate small wind and frost shelter-blocks, or areas of better soil quality for growing winter feed and crops.

The lambing percentage at Aspiring is now 115 per cent, which has been quite consistent for the last four years, but Randall thinks he could get it up to the mid-120s, in which case he'd be pretty happy, but 135 and he'd be very happy. Because the ewes are extensively stocked Randall won't see a lot of the lambs that perish, but then there's plenty of natural shelter, usually somewhere they can get out of the wind, and usually somewhere they can get out of puddles.

The ewes will stay together as one mob throughout the summer and autumn, the others being the two-tooths (the one-year-olds) and the light mob, both of which

The Mt Aspiring Station three-stand woolshed.

Opposite: Mixed-sex lambs destined for the freezer.

Above: Randall and Struan watch the last ewes make their way across the Matukituki; Randall's manuka hill-stick, mountain boots and heading dog Jess.

Two-tooth rams awaiting crutching.

are run on better pastures to bulk up before joining the main mob. They'll return to the sunny hill blocks via the woolshed in October for lambing, which for most rural properties in New Zealand is the busiest time of the year. But because of the topography of the lambing blocks, Aspiring is what you'd call a 'hands off' property in the spring, with an easy-care lambing management system. 'Basically, it means they're unassisted,' Randall explains. 'They're out on the hills and we don't really see them. Up here there's no such thing as a lambing beat.' On flat farm country shepherds on a lambing beat will go around between one and four times a day, checking every ewe. If a lamb is stuck, they'll pull it out. And if they have triplets, there's usually a weaker lamb they will take into the sheep yards and foster onto another ewe. 'Whereas up here the weakest triplet will just die,' Randall continues. 'And if the ewe has a lamb stuck, well, they'll both die. It's not a case of being cruel, it's just the type of country they're on. We cause more harm by upsetting the sheep and mismothering lambs than we do good. The ewes have also been bred and selected for it, so we don't have many problems with lambs getting stuck. It also helps that our sheep are quite toned and mobile, and probably because of our nutrition standard we don't get bigger lambs anyway.

'When we choose rams and ewe lambs to keep, we select the type of sheep that are going to be good for easy care. It's generally the shape — you don't want to have big heads and big shoulders. And we run our own recorded flock, so if we have problems with a ewe we won't keep it. Other than that it's just natural selection, if they can't pop out a lamb by themselves, they die — survival of the fittest.'

There have been a few changes over the last few years that have generally made life easier for the Aspinalls. In Jack, Jerry and John's time shearing was done after lambing, while the ewes were with their lambs. It's the more conventional husbandry practice but, as Sue Aspinall would find, year after year it was one of the most heartbreaking events on the farming calendar. 'You'd bring them in and have to draft the lambs one way and the ewes the other way, hoping they would all find their babies afterward. It was very hard work, and very unsettling. A lot didn't mother up again and we would end up with a whole lot of potty lambs that didn't have the best start in life really. So pre-lamb shearing is much better, as long as you get a good run of weather.'

Ultimately, animal husbandry anywhere comes down to feeding stock well. Lambing at Aspiring is around mid-October, and if it's a particularly cold spring they might not get any decent growth until November. The energy demand of lambing on the ewes is at its peak during the four weeks before lambing. If they're not fed well enough during this period the results are widely known. They will start using body fat, a by-product of which is the production of ketone toxins. Eventually, it can lead to what farmers call sleepy sickness and its telltale symptoms are stargazing, frothing from the mouth, staggering aimlessly away from the mob and progressing to a comatose state; eventually they'll just fall over and die. 'They're usually OK if they can have a good dose of sun on their backs and a belly full of tucker straight after they've been shorn,' says Sue. 'But some years you just get hit by cold southerly fronts, day after day. It's a real crunch time now that we shear them earlier in the season.'

There are still some years when it just doesn't go well, and it's from these years that the tough constitution of a high country farmer will be tested to its fullest. 'I actually found it harder as I got older and a bit more sensitive,' says Rachal Aspinall. 'One year after shearing we had a really cold time and lost a lot of stock in the conditions. I remember being so upset; it just didn't seem fair. I guess it just shows how tough it can be to know what's going to happen, to know what the weather is going to do and how to work around it. There's often not much you can do for them when you have so much stock spread out over such a large area. Particularly if there's a flood and you can't get across the creek to go up the valley — you'd be stupid to try. You just have to trust the stock have done the best they can to look after themselves. It was still hard when you saw stock losses from extreme weather events; when you actually saw the reality of dead animals, but it's a fact of life being a farmer. Dad was always very calm. I guess he just internalized it, and there was never the time to show it anyway.'

First light at Mill Creek.

Randall Aspinall, with the perennial ice of Mount Avalanche in the background.

Above: Dragonfly Peak. *Image courtesy of Danilo Hegg.*

Right: John Aspinall at Cattle Face in the late 1970s.

A waterfall beneath Cattle Face.
Opposite: The Cromwell calf sales.

With a dose of buckshot

With the sun low in the sky above the Pisa Range on a dry Otago afternoon, the rumbling, clanking sound of double-decker stock trucks down the Luggate highway signals the beginning of the annual calf sales in Cromwell. The Aspinalls have been making the trip to Cromwell every year since 1954, when 37 of their steers were auctioned off from the railhead for the first time. This year's no exception. Sue Aspinall has been to 32 calf sales, and only missed one since she arrived at Aspiring, for the birth of her son Randall.

The environment at Mt Aspiring Station requires tough, agile, medium-sized cattle. The herd is a Hereford-Angus cross and its grazing patterns complement their ruminating companions, tearing off long pastures with their tongues while the sheep get down to the sweet stuff. But the long, drawn-out winter can be tough on stock, and even tougher on their feed. Neither are things you want to gamble on in the Matukituki Valley.

Gary Walker has been the Mt Aspiring Station vet for the last 25 years, and knows the challenges the Aspinalls face better than most. 'It's a difficult environment up there. You have to stock it so that in the winter when the conditions are harshest you've got the least amount of stock. The climate's so cold they can't grow feed easily and it becomes a costly, labour-intensive operation to keep them going. They have good healthy cattle because they feed 'em well and get the basic animal health things right. And they don't push their luck. If there's surplus feed, they utilize it later. Cattle will stay alive for a long time with nothing to eat, as long as they can drink. But if you get it wrong and push them too hard, you'll come back to earth the following season when you put the bull back out, and I'll come along three or four months later and say, "Twenty per cent of these are dry because they're too thin."'

Stations like Aspiring tend to be called store breeding units. The potential for low-winter, and late-spring, growth is the major factor governing the way farmers operate in this type of country. In order to maximize potential they use good weather to produce large numbers from their base, and sell them all off at Cromwell before the winter sets in.

The week leading up to the sales is one of the busiest, noisiest times on Aspiring's calendar, as the seven- or eight-month-old calves are weaned off their mothers, separated in the cattle yards at Cameron Flat, and loaded onto stock trucks. The best heifer calves are kept to be reared as replacement breeding cows, and some of the male calves will join the group of mixed-age steers on the subalpine block for the winter, but the limits of the land always dictate how many can stay. For the Aspinalls, it's critical around 60 per cent of them are sold off the valley to low-lying, more intensive farms

A creek bed in the West Matukituki.

Auction list at the Cromwell calf sales.

at the end of every summer, and they're forced to take the going market price with its seasonal fluctuations.

The annual drive of sale calves and lambs to the railhead at Cromwell, some 70 miles away, was quite an event in Jerry's time. They had to be swum across the river three times, and driven to the Cromwell railhead at the rate of 10 miles a day. Annual drives with both sheep and cattle included traditional stop-offs at Glendhu, Wanaka, Luggate, Queensbury and Mount Pisa. Today, with the road improved all the way to Aspiring, the Aspinalls can have 230 calves at the saleyards before lunch.

It's a social affair, the Cromwell calf sales, as high country farmers from some of the most remote parts of New Zealand bring their families in for a day out, catching up with neighbours and relatives, and drafting up the next generation of young farmers. The real youngsters play all afternoon on old stock carts out the back while the bellowing exchanges of the auctioneers roll out in the background. The Plunket volunteers sell tea and asparagus rolls in the dug-out, something they've been doing for as long as it's been going. They'll be busy all afternoon this year — every pen in the yards is chocka.

Eyes on the bidding in the saleyards stand at Cromwell.

When everyone is seated in the old wooden stand, clouds of dust flick up as the herders start to bring in the mobs, sorted by their colour and size, for the bidding. Although the Aspinalls aren't here to buy, Sue Aspinall sits focused throughout the afternoon, jotting down the prices for each station's sales. It's something John always used to do, and because the sales contribute a quarter of the farm's annual profit, it's good to keep an eye on the field. 'It's interesting to know where they go,' says Sue. 'Some of the heifers might go for breeding, but the steers will all go for fattening. If I heard them say Maniototo, or South Otago, I would write that down. Or Nightcaps, they usually like to buy some. They must shift really well on their rolling country.'

Last year Aspiring's calf prices were down $20 or so from the previous year, but more often than not Aspiring calves fetch the second or third highest prices at the sales. They're lauded by the auctioneers as having a 'beautiful temperament', something Randall thinks is due to the volume of people over Aspiring land each year. 'Calm cows means calm calves,' he says. 'Often they're so quiet you'll try to push them through the yards and they just don't move!'

Throughout the year the cattle at Aspiring are free to roam the flats along the

Auctioneers and prospective buyers above the sale pens.

length of the Matukituki River and regularly come in contact with people and, to the surprise of first-time visitors to the valley, the cattle will rarely be in a hurry to shift off the road. They're a docile bunch, these Aspiring cows. But it wasn't always so. The back-block stations around the Alps in New Zealand remained largely unfenced until four-wheel drive trucks allowed for the bulk transport of materials. Instead farmers relied mostly on natural boundaries — gorges, rivers, cliffs and dense bush. As a result the cattle lived an undomesticated existence; they had a nervous inclination and were difficult to muster. In Jerry Aspinall's time the Aspiring cattle were made up of shorthorns, feeding on low-intensity native pastures spread as far as the avalanche plain of Shovel Flat, glaring with wild eyes from the bush. It was a daunting job to rein them in.

'I fenced off some of the bush areas cattle were wont to charge into, but I couldn't fence them all,' Jerry recalled. 'Up the West Matukituki above Rob Roy there were 50 or so cows that were easy to manage but some 150 plus were as wild as could be and charged over, under, past or through anything and anybody that tried to prevent them from getting into their bush retreats.

'Using the Cascade Hut as a base I spent many days just tracking and dogging cattle out of the bush. I also resorted to homemade bombs consisting of small lemonade bottles filled with blasting powder, coarse sand and a length of fuse. Although comparatively harmless, the resulting boom, flash and cloud of smoke upset their sense of security in the bush, so much so that they trampled over each other in their haste. In order to protect myself and my horse against charging animals I cut down the barrel and stock of an old shotgun and carried it on a holster on my saddle. This was not used injudiciously, but on much of the rough terrain a beast could go faster than a horse, and if it got too close, and persisted with a mean look in its eye, a dose of buckshot helped it decide who was boss.'

Each year the Cromwell township would tremble at the sight of those cattle beasts from the mountains. They thought nothing of charging horses and dogs and, if startled, they would stampede and run themselves to the point of exhaustion. 'They were very scary around motor cars and particularly people on foot,' Jerry added. 'Even at an early age it was my job to ride in front of the mob, trying to look unworried and unconcerned, and hold them down to a walk. I had to learn to anticipate what their reactions were likely to be and prevent trouble before it started.

'One year a truck with squealing brakes startled a hundred cattle into the lake at Glendhu Bay. After several hours in the water 80 landed on Ewings Peninsula, 10 struggled ashore here and there, while 10 more just swam aimlessly around in circles until they drowned. Going through Cromwell was tricky and at the bridge, after traffic had been stopped, it was my job to go in front while the cattle were forced on behind

Earmarked heifer calves kept back from the saleyards as replacements, and steers kept for fattening.

me with dog and whip. The hollow sound of their feet on the decking upset them and it took the half mile to the railway yards to get them under control again. One year three big scary steers "broke" back through town and across the golf course during a ladies tournament. Some ladies maintained for years afterwards that those steers chased a car with red wheels!'

Soon after the calves are sold off in Cromwell, their mothers still bellowing day and night, planning is in place to bring down the Aspiring steers from Mill Creek. The steers, a mixed-age group of young castrated males, are raised together on some of the tougher blocks at Aspiring where the cows don't do as well. They spend the summer in the hanging valleys above the bush line and the winter on Cattle Face. Mill Creek had originally been under licence to a farm near the head of Lake Wanaka, at the end of the Matukituki River. The farmer, Harry Barker, used to drive small herds up through the bush in the summer months. But it's tough country, and when Harry's son Ernie approached a more flappable age he voluntarily released his grazing lease to Jerry Aspinall. Jerry was apprehensive about Mill Creek at first.

'I had never been into Mill Creek before, but had heard stories of the great herds of hundreds of deer that had been seen in there in the 1920s. One day I went over the tops, 5500 feet into the left-hand branch, and camped the night under a bivvy rock I had heard about. On the way down into the valley I didn't know where the tracks were, but followed a herd of stags down on the assumption that where they could go so could I. It was very steep and was the last time I entertained that particular theory.'

Understandably, getting his first mobs of 100 cattle up through the dense beech forest and over the tussock ridges 2000 feet above the river flats — then back down again at the end of summer — took some practice, for steers and shepherds alike. 'We took some that had been there before to act as leaders. In some respects cattle have great memories. The weaker ones had to be nursed along and given plenty of time or else they would become overtired and collapse. For the first few years the muster out was quite an effort. Breakfast at 1 a.m. then a three-mile ride to the foot of the track, followed by a climb up through the bush and tussock by torchlight to arrive on the ridge above the gorge at daybreak. Usually done in April, this work was harder if there had been an early fall of snow. Even so, a light autumn frost down by the homestead could mean frozen, rock-hard ground up in Mill Creek.'

Frost or not, it was always a race against time to get out of the bush before nightfall. Some years the musterers would take sleeping bags and camp out in the bush the night before, but when the new homestead was built closer to the valley entrance, the musterers set out before dawn and could make it back to the homestead just as the kitchen lights were coming on. Now the Aspinalls use a helicopter to take the musterers and their dogs up in the morning, but they still have to walk the cattle out through the

The Cromwell calf sales.

bush and count them back through the gate and, if the tallies are more than three or four short, they'll be going back up in a helicopter for the stragglers that won't survive the winter snows and avalanches.

Surveying the cloud lifting off the mountains at the end of the Aspiring run on the east branch there's a sharp winter chill in the air, and a new layer of snow drifts about the high ridges of Cattle Face. 'Bad day to be a steer,' Randall says, looking on from his truck. In May each year, after the steers have been brought down from Mill Creek, they are taken up the east branch and driven high onto the station frontier where they will spend the winter. It's a tough existence, foraging on the tussock slopes; too high to feed hay out, at least by foot, and it takes two or three efforts over consecutive days to drive them up above the bush line. For the most part they endure it well, but they won't be completely abandoned up Cattle Face.

Each year the Aspinalls will expect to come up for the tough, killing work of snow-raking. Heavy snow dumps cause deep drifts that can quickly bury cattle, and snow-

Monique's dogs, from left: Spit, Toot and Cruise.

raking is the term used in the high country to describe the job of getting them out. On low-lying country, paths can be made with a tractor, but if it's at altitude, the only option is on foot. The state of the snow depends on how quickly you get to them — if it's still light and powdery, stock can be led out with relative ease, but if it's had time to thaw and freeze, a hard iron crust will form. On shady faces it can also become deep and crystalline, and won't pack beneath your weight. In any event, the snow-raker must use sticks and boots to beat a path out of the snow for the stock to follow, willingly or not, depending on their condition and how long they've been stuck.

It's easier to get to them now with helicopters in the valley, but in times gone by stock could be stuck for up to four weeks before help arrived. Cattle have a remarkable constitution in such weather, but Jerry would come to note that when cattle are snowed in they just stand in one place, slowly suffering from starvation, the cold and a lack of drinking water. 'After four, five or six weeks of this they become stiff, immobile, uncaring and just die.'

It doesn't *sound* all that pleasant, but for the workers at Aspiring it was often their experiences snow-raking they would come to treasure the most. It was also a rite of passage for the Aspinall children growing up, to snow-rake at Cattle Face, as Rachal Aspinall recalls. 'We were always told by Dad, "Whatever you do, don't drop the shovel!" It was hard, hard work, and at the end of the day you're so bone-tired from pushing through the snow and yelling at the steers. When they're going well they will keep moving, but they might get to a stage where you might have to turn them a different way, or they might just be being stubborn, at which stage you have to dig down until they can see the ground so they know it is safe.

'But it was a wonderful experience to be up there in those elements, and so much satisfaction knowing you helped them and got them to a place where they were going to survive. Walking around through the shady gullies was reasonably dangerous because if you did slip, there was quite a wee way to go and not much to stop you. I would always take it slow, not like Dad, who could pick a path and just stride up the hill. He knew it like the back of his hand. He probably took the odd slide, but it didn't scare him. We used to worry a bit, especially if he had gone to Cattle Face in winter when it got dark much earlier, but he knew how to respect the land as well, so he didn't need to fear it.'

With farming running deep through their veins, the Aspinalls have never been particularly interested in profiting from the tourism industry. But during the winter they have often allowed heliskiers to fly off their land on the front face between Mill Creek and McGills, Fog Peak behind the homestead and up past the road end at Mount Tyndall. The deal has always been that the Aspinalls receive some helicopter time from the operators in return. It's seldom used for recreation; snow-raking at

John Aspinall snow-raking for stragglers at Mill Creek.

Cattle Face will be one of the few times the Aspinalls take advantage of it. Jerry would sometimes go up with top-dressing fixed-wings, when the opportunity came up, but spotting cattle from a plane meant you still had to walk up from the bottom to get to them, and it wasn't without its hazards anyway.

'There were many occasions when Tex and his co-pilots came over to put out top-dressing or take me up cattle-spotting. Once, having dropped rocksalt up on Cattle Face, the tight turns and manoeuvres became a little much for me and a bout of air sickness caused me to lose my false teeth somewhere in the miles of beech forest spread out below.'

The technological advance of the aviation industry has been a godsend to many high country farmers, landing dogs and musterers virtually anywhere in the mountains. Charlie Ewing farmed around the precipices at Cattle Flat station for

The Mt Aspiring Station steers in their summer block at Mill Creek.

40 years, and in the 1980s set up a helicopter business from his property called Aspiring Helicopters. 'It's a very tough business,' Charlie explains. 'Most of our work is in the Matuki, but we look after an area from Milford to Haast. Farm work is a very small amount of our work each year, but for those few hours, the contribution to running the farm is huge. Often on my way home if I'm the only one flying, my eyes are watching what's happening on the farm the whole way. Those few minutes become invaluable. If you see something wrong, you fix it — just like that.

'Snow-raking cattle at 5000 feet was quite an art. I would be called in times of heavy snow to fly John up, mainly up to the Cattle Face area. He usually had a young shepherd with him. They would get out and unload dogs, shovels and hill bags and I can tell you this is in seriously steep country, but John with his quietly determined nature had a special skill in rescuing his stock. My understanding is that he never had any mishaps, and that is quite an achievement given the steep country and deep snow he had to contend with. He would often return from these missions well after dark.'

It was these nights more than ever that Sue would wait at the homestead, wondering if her husband was going to make it home safely. 'John taught me to cope with the elements and he wouldn't think that anyone would worry if he wasn't back before dark,' says Sue. 'But for someone who wasn't brought up in the high country and didn't have neighbours close by it wasn't easy — I used to worry a lot. I still used to worry about him right up until we left. I worried the most when he was out by himself, as opposed to two of them, because surely they both couldn't be hurt. They might have got the truck stuck or the tractor stuck or something. But once they went out the gate in the morning I often had no idea where they were. There were no radios like there are now. And John might tell me where he intended to go — but that wasn't always where he ended up.

'I would sometimes go looking for him. Sometimes I would get to the gate and he would turn up, but it was always a difficult one — how long would you wait for somebody to come home? Your mind just goes overtime. And then of course when they do come home you're all fired up — "Where have you been? What have you been doing?" And all he would say is, "I've just been finishing a job." Sometimes Charlie Ewing would drop him off by helicopter to either of our high spots up above the bush in the winter and afterwards Charlie would call in at night and ask, "Is he home yet?" And I would say, "No ..." There were some worrying times.'

Feed reserves

A winter feed wagon.

Because of the vagaries of the weather in the Matukituki Valley and its indifference to the needs of its livestock, January and February have always been one of the busiest times of the year, and it has always coincided with the peak season for tramping and climbing. Many trampers remember lending a hand with haymaking over the decades, particularly in the early days before alpine huts were built up the valley, perhaps in return for a bed and a packhorse. 'Sometimes the wind blows the cut grass out of the paddocks and even buries the fences with it,' Jerry would tell them. 'On other occasions whirlwinds or "williwaws" will sweep through a paddock of cut hay and whirl it 500 or even 4000 feet up into the sky.' Normally, the Aspinalls will make 500 bales of hay a year, 350 kilos each, but they didn't make as many this year because of the unusually dry weather in February. As a reserve, the station makes its own vacuum silage by loading cut grass onto a plastic sheet until it builds up into a large stack, at which time another sheet is put over the top and the two joined together to form an airtight envelope. The air is then pumped out to stop the grass from oxidizing and rotting. It will keep for years, as the cattle are finding out this season, although sometimes it takes a while for them to find an appetite for fermented fodder.

Feeding out at Aspiring begins in June, and the Aspinalls often find they have to feed out hay on an almost daily basis until the middle of October, or later, if the spring growth is behind schedule. Before machinery stepped in, the job of haymaking and feeding out was a cold and labour-intensive exercise, and as soon as the Aspinall children could reach the steering wheel they were out there lending a hand, as Catie Aspinall recalls: 'We learnt how to steer the truck from five or six years old. I wouldn't say we learnt how to drive it properly because our legs weren't long enough to reach the pedals, but it was still easier for Dad to set the truck off in first gear and let us just steer the way around the paddock.'

With a tractor, hydraulic arms and a Robertson feed-wagon trailer, the job of feeding out on frosty mornings has been made a lot simpler for Randall, yet it remains vital to the livelihood that he's there rain or shine, feeding out over the long winter ahead.

Cows on the road.

Autumn, Mt Aspiring Station.

Mt Aspiring Station truck.

Opposite: Mount Aspiring in 1963 from Bevan Col, an alpine pass between the Matukituki and Waipara.

The Big Fellow

Mount Aspiring is one of the crown jewels of New Zealand's Southern Alps. At 3033 metres it is 200 metres higher than any other peak for 150 kilometres and it is the only one over 3000 metres outside Aoraki/ Mount Cook National Park. Maori called it Tititea (Glistening Peak) and Makahi Ta Rakiwhanoa (The wedge belonging to the demi-god Tu Te Rakiwhanoa). The government surveyor Turnbull Thomson called his lofty conical peak Mount Aspiring, and mountaineers revered it as the Matterhorn of the South, the Silver Cone and the Monarch of the Cold Lakes; farmer John Aspinall lived beneath its frozen precipices for almost 60 years, and he always knew it simply as the Big Fellow. Whatever they called it, and whatever their purpose – botanists, geologists, scientists, seasoned climbers or those wanting just to conquer their fear of heights – from the very beginning the access route to the Big Fellow was through Mt Aspiring Station. Be it a waving hand from across the river or a back country banquet, many of those from the great influxes of climbers in the twentieth century will remember the Aspinalls and their devotion to the mountain at the head of the valley.

For the mountaineers, the Aspinalls provided indispensable assistance, not least by allowing access across their land. But they would also act as guides, giving out early maps of bivouacs along the way, carrying food, ropes, pick-axes and blankets by

Above and opposite: Pack teams in 1939.

packhorse, cooking over open fires for dozens at a time and, latterly, helping to build the first alpine huts. Such was their contribution even in the earliest years that in 1932 a Dunedin tramper named Howard Boddy named a 2300-metre mountain at the head of the east branch after Jack Aspinall: Aspinall Peak.

The homestead became a place where adventurous journeys started and finished and, in the summer, often one group was returning to the homestead from the mountains just as another arrived. For the Aspinalls the groups of mountaineers, coming and going, broke the isolation of the valley, sharing their stories of good and evil in the hills, their triumphs and their tragedies, above all growing a mutual knowledge of the environment and the forces of nature.

The first decades of pioneering ascents around Mount Aspiring were marred by the world at war and the Great Depression. Gear was primitive and loads were heavy — a climber might be carrying over 50 kilograms on his back when he collapsed on the front porch of the homestead. The Aspinalls, their station hacks and their proximity to the mountains became of great importance to these first expeditions. The very first ascent of Mount Aspiring was via the western face and north-west ridge in 1909 by the Englishman Bernard Head, in just his second season of New Zealand mountaineering. In his party were New Zealand guides Alex Graham and Jack Clarke, the latter of whom had also been a member of the first party to climb Mount Cook.

By horse and cart down a dirt road from Wanaka they stopped for lunch at Theo Russell's Cattle Flat Station, not long before the famous back country cook Jack Aspinall was employed there. The trio then rode as far as the Aspiring homestead, then occupied by Duncan Macpherson, and onward on foot up the east branch of the Matukituki with the assistance of Duncan's packhorse. They camped at Junction Flat, where they were beset for days by rain, and when a clearing permitted a brief

Climbing camps in 1932.

exchange with the monarch itself, they could see no obvious way up. They named the flat Disappointment Camp, before backtracking down the valley. They would eventually make the ascent after swagging their way through the bush above Pearl Flat up the west branch, where Duncan turned back to the homestead. They launched the final ascent of Aspiring from nearby French Mountain and across the mighty Bonar Glacier.

In the days after 23 November 1909 reports echoed down the Matukituki Valley of the first ascent of Mount Aspiring. And on the 26th, a telegram made it official, newspaper headlines bringing the 'Conquest of Mount Aspiring' to a captivated New Zealand public. 'Mount Aspiring has for a long time been considered one of the unclimbable mountains of New Zealand', the *West Coast Times* article read. 'There were quite a number of New Zealand mountains that came under that heading — but one by one they have yielded to the persevering attacks of the Alpine climber.' In a cruel twist of fate Captain Head would later perish on the mounds of the Gallipoli peninsula in 1915. But on a plaque in his memory at Aspiring Hut, there is a passage from a poet called Geoffrey Winthrop Young, himself a climber, immortalizing the pioneering achievement:

> What if I live no more those kingly days?
> Their night sleeps with me still.
> I dream my feet upon the starry ways;
> My heart rests in the hill.
> I may not grudge the little left undone:
> I hold the heights, I keep the dreams I won.

Mount Aspiring climbing party, 1929.

The weather god was kind enough to the first party ascending Aspiring's ridges, but for the second, Tawhirimatea was not so accommodating. The attempt came in 1913, led by the experienced Samuel Turner, via a similar route to the Head expedition. From the outset it became a climb of attrition, totalling some 60 hours. In Turner's amateur climbing career he had surmounted the Matterhorn in Switzerland, discovered a new mountain range in Siberia, climbed the highest mountain in the Americas, Aconcagua, in record time, and climbed Mount Cook solo, but as far as he was concerned the ascent of Aspiring was one of the most difficult climbs he had attempted — much more precarious than anything in the Swiss Alps and wetter than any climb he had ever engaged in.

The climbing party had been storm-bound near the head of the West Matukituki River for six days before they set off at 6 a.m. on 10 March and, what's more, Turner's three companions hadn't any previous experience on an ice slope. They arrived near the Quarterdeck Saddle where they set up a small mountain tent, just as Captain Head had done in November 1909. After resting for a few hours they continued climbing throughout the night and through a dense sea of fog. They continued without sleep, and after hours of slow step-cutting across glaciers — a method preceding the use of crampons, by which a climber cut footholds into the ice with a pick — crossing snow bridges and evading crevasses, they reached partway up the north-west ridge of Aspiring. In the closing darkness and with an alpine storm building, they finally reached the summit at 5 p.m. on 11 March.

Exhausted, they spent only minutes at the top, greeted by thunderous wind,

Mount Aspiring, August 1947. *Image courtesy of Whites Aviation Collection, Alexander Turnbull Library.*

howling in a mire of sleet. With no hope of returning to their camp, they made do without food, hunched around a crevice in the rocks above the north-west buttress, exposed to all the might of the heavens. All they could do was wait until dawn. 'The loud shivering and chattering of teeth by each member of the party was discomforting, so I started a mountain song in which I made them all join and repeat from time to time during the night,' Turner called to mind. The night in the open was an experience a 'man does once in a lifetime, but never again'. When they finally reached their camp on 12 March they lit a fire in the tent door, which they kept going all night to keep warm, just one blanket between them. They finally got to sleep at 3 a.m., by which time they had done without it for 70 hours.

For Turner, the ascent was yet another remarkable feat, but it was perhaps overshadowed by the ambition of his three Kiwi companions, baptized by fire: Hodgkinson, Murrell and Robertson, three who had tackled one of New Zealand's most formidable peaks with scarcely any experience between them. 'But this is the resourceful stuff New Zealanders are made of,' Turner concluded. 'They will have a shot at anything, no matter how difficult of success or certain of failure.' In his book *The Conquest of the New Zealand Alps*, published almost 10 years later, Turner heaped praise on the pioneers of New Zealand mountaineering:

Mount Aspiring, surrounded by a wilderness of perpetual ice and snow.

> The world is just realizing what very difficult and inaccessible mountains there are in New Zealand, also the exceptional mountaineering skill and endurance a climber must put forth to gain success. The skill of New Zealand pioneers in the last ten years would gain success on any mountains in the world.

Turner's prophecies proved true over the coming decades. The pioneers of New Zealand mountaineering began to excel, they took their prowess to the world, and they proved fitter and stronger than anyone else. It was such fitness and endurance that culminated in a generation of world-class mountaineers, not least Sir Edmund Hillary.

By now it was very clear how important the station homestead was to those attempting to climb Mount Aspiring. Turner himself had declared it was the most inaccessible mountain in New Zealand, and 'whatever equipment is taken it has to be remembered that the explorer and climber in New Zealand must move much faster than in Switzerland, or anywhere else I know of, owing to the low level one starts to climb from'. To get to the base near enough to climb the Big Fellow it was necessary to have two base camps, one at Pembroke and one up the West Matukituki Valley. Being the final inhabitation between Pembroke and Aspiring, and the first coming back, the coming decades would see an influx of mountaineers to the station like it had never seen before. Luckily for the mountaineers, Jack and Amy were incredibly hospitable people, setting a precedent for the rest of the century, inviting almost anyone who came within sight of the homestead to stay the night, or at least to share the mutton. Amy was also known to love a game of bridge, and no doubt revelled in the steady stream of climbers waiting for the weather to clear.

The third ascent was in November 1927, and included a young climber named Roland Ellis. For the Aspinalls it was the start of a lifelong friendship with the Ellis family, who spent most Christmas and Easter holidays at the homestead, the families learning from each other the outdoor skills required to survive in an inhospitable environment. In 1992 Murray Ellis, Roland's son, wrote the foreword to Jerry Aspinall's autobiography *Farming under Aspiring*, in which he heaped praise on the skills he learnt about the outdoors from Jerry, which would stand him in good stead on the first overland crossing of Antarctica with Edmund Hillary.

Two years after his first encounter with Roland Ellis, Jack thought he might as well give it a go himself. And so the fourth ascent up Mount Aspiring was made in 1929 by guide Frank Alack, Jack Aspinall and Lillian Familton of Oamaru, the first woman to attempt the climb. Jack had promised to take the pair's gear to the planned high bivouac, but when given the choice of continuing on or returning back to the station, Jack just decided to keep going. Frank Alack would later recall the episode in his 1963 book *Guide Aspiring*. 'For a man on his first peak he did very well, though I did hear his broad Lancashire voice often bemoaning the absence of a "handful of tussock".' The unlikely trio camped at French Ridge before using crampons to attempt the top via the north-west ridge, and they did so in torrid weather. 'By the time we gained it, the top of our peak had disappeared in the clouds,' Alack wrote:

> As we scrambled upward, the sky-sized, bleak, grey blanket was slowly descending. It would not be pleasant when we met. Jack Aspinall was not accustomed to this sort of thing and we were all on the soft side from several days of sitting in camp, but there was no question of them asking to turn back.

Soon the group was swallowed up in a thick cloud of sleet. The swirling white hell at the top coated them with so much ice and snow that they were all but indistinguishable from the landscape until movement gave them away. 'Icicles were hanging from Jack's bushy eyebrows. It was almost useless to wipe them away; in a few minutes they were back again. He should have had his brows clipped before we started,' Alack said.

Left: Julia Aspinall and Christopher Aspinall during their morning lessons at the homestead in the 1960s.
Right: James K Baxter at the Mt Aspiring Station homestead in 1949. *Image courtesy of Archives New Zealand: National Publicity Studios Collection.*

The trio arrived back at the station homestead full of the elation which wells up after a period of sustained and rugged effort, and just in time to celebrate Jack's birthday. The next two generations of Aspinalls were to follow in their forebear's footsteps, 'persuaded to go beyond the bush and tussock slopes where for years I had chased animals,' as Jerry said. Jerry made the ascent in 1954 and John in 2008, but it is the hospitality those generations showed the alpine community that the Aspinalls will be remembered for most of all, although such generous ways weren't always without a catch.

In 1943, soon after Jack's death, Paul Powell arrived at Mt Aspiring Station as

a single employee, working for Jerry in return for a bed beneath the peak that had captivated his mind for 15 years, a case of self-diagnosed 'Aspiring madness'. On seeing Powell with a battered rucksack at his feet and an ice-axe in hand, Jerry was said to remark, no doubt with a smirk on his face: 'I'm glad to see you've brought your hoe — there's plenty of weeding to be done up at the homestead.'

Powell would write extensively about his experiences climbing the peaks around Mt Aspiring Station in his book *Men Aspiring*, and his stories have long been the companion of climbers and trampers in the huts, tents and bivouacs of New Zealand's high places. Like many others before and after Powell, the alpine community came to treasure their time at Mt Aspiring Station, and there's a paragraph in his book that all who harbour the search for beauty in these hills should heed some 70 years on:

> The values at Aspiring station were those of all who knew the mountains; in storm, shelter; in trouble, help. This then was the link that had grown between the Aspinalls, mountaineers, and the people who came to the Matukituki Valley. The tradition was 23 years old when I first arrived, and I know that it will flourish as long as there is an Aspinall at Mt Aspiring Station.

Nowadays Mount Aspiring can be reached from the high-altitude Colin Todd Hut or a bivouac on the Bonar Glacier in about 12 hours, or 16 hours from French Ridge Hut, with guided roped-glacier travel and varying degrees of difficulty to reach the summit. Even so, Mount Aspiring by the north-west ridge is still a serious undertaking. 'There should be no fixed aids, but there is no room for ambivalence — you are entirely on its terms,' John had said. It also requires a good level of fitness and an experienced guide with whom you must place all of your faith. 'Climbing mountains is one of those things that requires you to separate out the emotional side of your brain from the logical side,' says Phil Melchior, who climbed Mount Aspiring in 2003. 'From the emotional side of your brain you look down — when you are going up the Ramp, for instance — and you realize your feet are held on to the mountainside by the front points of your crampons and when you look between your legs there's nothing there. All of your instincts are saying this is the sort of thing your mother told you never to do, but then the logical side of your brain says, well, actually, you are with a guide and on a rope and he's got you safe, and you need to trust your equipment and just carry on.'

Phil is now the Land Search and Rescue New Zealand Chairman and a Wanaka branch volunteer. He also got to know John Aspinall by working on a number

The avalanche plain of Shovel Flat and, beyond it, Pearl Flat, named after Jack Aspinall's packhorse Pearl.

of operations in the Matukituki after he moved to Wanaka, chasing his love of the environment. 'You don't have to go up very far before you get into solitude. If you compare it to Europe, most of the time you're picking your way over other people's ropes. You don't get that in New Zealand.'

If things go awry in the Matukituki, however, solitude can be your worst enemy. 'The big thing in New Zealand is people underestimating the way the weather can change,' says Phil. 'They also often underestimate the difficulty of the terrain, and what a change it makes. The biggest problem areas in recent years have been the Cascade Saddle and Mount Aspiring, and climbing accidents usually happen on the way down. The Saddle is a steep and reasonably demanding haul up, but coming down something steep is always more difficult than going up. People get too close to the edge, and they don't consider the conditions appropriately. If you slip in any of these places, your ability to recover your margin of error is very, very small.

'Personally and organizationally, we believe people should get out there and experience our back country, test themselves and all the rest of it. But from a search and rescue point of view the message we are always preaching is be aware of the risks you are taking — take considered risks and not unconsidered ones. For me there is a great feeling of accomplishment just from having got as far as you've got, whether that's the top or not doesn't always matter. If you turn back for a good reason — and being completely exhausted in my book is a good reason — then that's what you do, but you've given it a good crack.' Today Search and Rescue Wanaka will receive anything from between 35 to 50 operations a year, 80 per cent of which will be in Mount Aspiring National Park. Of those, around five will be fatalities and of those the Cascade Saddle and the Bonar Glacier would account for at least one.

The search and rescue operations in the Matukituki are organized by the police in Wanaka, liaising with helicopter operators like Charlie Ewing at Cattle Flat Station. 'It's become quite an adventurous wee town,' says Charlie. 'But the improvement in the technology in the last five years has been incredible. We used to fly around for days looking for someone. It does happen, but now most times they'll be carrying beacons, and the coordinates will take you straight to them. If the weather is too bad we just can't go, but Wanaka has a very strong search and rescue team. They have a lot of mountain guys, fishing guys, lake guys — if we have one in a waterfall we have a canyon group, or in a rapid we have a rapid group ... Then we have our "bushies", and our alpine cliff rescue team. But it's important to always use local knowledge. There is always someone that knows a bit more, and it's best to slow down and pick up on it.'

Top: John Aspinall with guide Guy Cotter on John's ascent of Mount Aspiring in 2008, with the head of the Waiototo in the background. Bottom: Tents on the Bonar Glacier. *Image courtesy of Danilo Hegg.*

Mount Aspiring from Glendhu Bay.

Historically, the Aspinalls were the first port of call in mountain emergencies. For a long time, the homestead across the river had the only radio contact for miles around, and the Aspinalls would relay messages back and forth with Dunedin throughout the night. The Aspinall children were involved in search and rescue operations from an early age — John would remember using a station horse to retrieve a frostbitten climber at just 11 years old, and throughout the year his siblings counted many missions up the river in miserable conditions to get supplies as far as Aspiring Hut, often the base of operations.

Other times, when the river was too high to cross, the kids remember their father Jerry on high alert. 'Dad was always looking out for people stuck on the other side of the river,' says Julia. 'For example, when we lived in the east branch there were some people stuck on the other side of the East Matuki. Dad saw them there and knew they

were stuck so he tied some tea, sugar, matches and fire-lighting tablets to a rock and threw them over so they could make a cup of tea. They were obviously a bit ignorant, though, because when they got out, they asked, "What were those vitamin tablets you threw over?"'

To this day, the Aspinall homestead is still the first habitation climbers encounter, coming out of the mountains. 'Historically, if push comes to shove, they're the ones who are there,' says guide Geoff Wayatt. 'New ones coming in wouldn't have the historical context that the Aspinalls have, and John would always put his hand up for search parties, giving up his day. In fact, we've even landed helicopters on their front lawn and treated patients in the homestead. They never, ever questioned their involvement in the mountains.'

The Matukituki Valley, gateway to the second most glaciated region in New Zealand, with Mount Avalanche centre-right and behind it, just visible to the right of the photograph, Mount Aspiring.

Flying hammers

There's a heritage of back country huts in New Zealand unlike any other place in the world. Around 1400 huts dot the remote bush and alpine landscape, unlocking some of the most valuable scenery the nation has to offer. Around 750 of New Zealand's huts were built for animal control, 500 for sheep musterers and 150 for tramping and recreation. Nowadays huts can be maintained by helicopter, but most were built quite literally off the backs of the alpine and high country farmer community. On Mt Aspiring Station and in the Matukituki Valley there are seven brilliant examples of the quirky, the outlandish and the time-honoured classics.

Nestled on a grassy slope beside the current Mt Aspiring Station homestead there's a small hut with a green roof, white walls, and a sign with Niger Hut written in bold. For most passers-by this old Tourist Board hut would go largely unnoticed, but its location once marked the end of the road before a small bridle track continued on around the bluffs and up the valley. In times gone by, Niger Hut was a haven for travellers if the river was up, or if a slip blocked the way and, in the early days, there was an unwritten law that any person using a hut always left tea, sugar and dry firewood for the next visitor. When the Aspinalls lived across the river, unexpected visitors would light a smoke

From left: Cascade Hut and Colin Todd Hut.

From left: Aspiring Hut and Cascade Hut.

signal from Niger Hut, three miles downstream. A packhorse was readily sent over to investigate, as it often meant someone had brought up days' and weeks' worth of mail and newspapers.

Ten kilometres from Niger Hut is Raspberry Hut in a paddock at the bottom of the slopes leading up to Sharks Tooth Peak. Before four-wheel drives made lighter work of the journey up and down the valley, Jerry, and Jack before him, would use the hut to shelter from storms after long days on the hills, or nights when the river came up unexpectedly.

For 21 years it was also used by the Silva family over the summer holidays. Raspberry remains full of childhood memories for the five Silva kids, their father telling stories long into the night by candlelight, their mother making bread over the camp oven. There was no running water or electricity, and evenings would be busy collecting firewood in order to boil the billy after days swimming, kayaking and tramping. 'But when the weather was bad you had to be indoors,' remembers Jeremy Silva. 'The hut was staked down with waratahs and number 8 wire. In a decent wind it was absolutely frightening because the wind would actually lift it up and take a strain on the wire. So the hut was very primitive. The beds were made of manuka poles and sheep netting, with a mattress on top. But there were always things to do.

'The standard instructions for anyone coming up from town were to bring milk, bread, lettuce and tomatoes. My mother would have to disguise the meat a bit because it wouldn't always be quite right, a bit green, and the butter a bit rancid, but as children we didn't know any better. We did a lot of fishing and ate a lot of trout when we caught them. I don't eat trout any more! I remember shooting some Canada geese with Jerry one day because we were so sick of trout. But we had to cook it for 24 hours, it was so tough. We also ate the odd rabbit and hare, but spaghetti on toast was the favourite, and Maggi soup as well.'

Two hours' walk from Raspberry Hut, tucked in at the forest edge beneath the Cascade Saddle, are the instantly recognizable twin chimneys of Cascade Hut, the next hut up the valley. The hut was built in 1932 by the Otago section of the New Zealand Alpine Club on station land, and actually comprised two huts from Dunedin, joined together with a porch tacked onto the front. As a young boy Jerry remembers packing food and tents for the 'hungry hordes' of workers, and then in 1940 packing timber up to the head of the valley, from where it was transported on climbers' backs to build the first hut at French Ridge. The original Cascade Hut is still in use by the Alpine Club, while French Ridge Hut has been rebuilt several times, the latest in 1999, slightly lower than its original location, but still at 1463 metres.

Following the Second World War, hut-building in the back country took on a new lease of life, and soon 'hammers were flying within sight of Aspiring', Paul Powell noted. This second wind is no more epitomized than by the magnificence of Aspiring Hut on the banks of Cascade Creek. Grey schist rock was sledged by station hacks

Niger Hut.

from the flats for the walls, and building commenced in 1946, with Jerry, Amy and Pat all included in the building party. The location of the hut, on the flats before the bush, was the logical place for a base camp for those making the ascent of Mount Aspiring, as it was a tough slog through the bush from there on until Shovel Flat. The hut opened in 1949 with the capacity to sleep 30 to 40 people, and it was here that James K Baxter is said to have written 'Poem in the Matukituki Valley'. Today, a plaque in Aspiring Hut commemorates the vision and the energies of members of the Otago section of the New Zealand Alpine Club, their families and friends, who, 'with generous support of the Aspinall family', built this magnificent hut between 1946 and 1949.

In 1947 the first materials were carried up the Otago section of the New Zealand Alpine Club valley for the Liverpool Hut, which was completed in 1953 and replaced on the same site in 2009. In 1960 Colin Todd Hut was built at the base of the north-west ridge of Aspiring at 1799 metres, accessed across the Bonar Glacier from French Ridge Hut. A replacement was built in 1996, and although by this time helicopters made the task a tad more trifling, John Aspinall continued the proud tradition of hut-building in the Matukituki.

At the time, Stu Thorne was involved with the Department of Conservation. 'When I was involved earlier with the tracks and huts we built a few new huts and one of them was Colin Todd. John was very interested in that so he came along and helped us on a few occasions. I remember one time we were trying to put the foundations down and we had to get rid of quite a bit of rock — it's really high up — but John was more than happy to get on the jackhammer for most of the day, just drilling holes in rock. He was happy as. Just for nothing, he just wanted to be involved.'

Top to bottom: Aspiring Hut, Raspberry Hut.

IMV

Helicopter flying through a
hanging valley at Mill Creek.

Hunting in the Matukituki Valley.

Old deer yards on Mt Aspiring Station.

Opposite: Chamois hunting in one of the hanging valleys above Mt Aspiring Station.

Bandits in the hills

Hunting is a tradition that has always been fostered in the Matukituki Valley. Since 1920 the Aspinalls have been keen hunters in their own right, and have always permitted and encouraged hunting on their land. It's part of their underlying philosophy, of sharing their love for the environment, fostering the cultures of recreational use in the valley, maintaining a heritage and, more importantly, keeping the balance.

'It's amazing, isn't it?' Gary Walker, the Mt Aspiring Station vet, leans forward, chortling through the headset, grinning over the noise of the rotors lifting the helicopter above the beech trees and the snowy spurs of the Matukituki. On any other day hunting at Mill Creek the Walkers would have already been hiking up the cattle tracks for some hours, whacking through the bush long before daybreak, but this is something of a sentimental trip for Gary and his son Mike — and Gary's knees 'just aren't what they used to be'.

A plume of snow and ice erupts, the Robinson R44 hovers to a standstill — landing the way only a helicopter can — and the Walkers dismount with their rifles and hill-sticks. At an altitude of 1200 metres, Mill Creek is what they call a hanging valley, a gorge with a flattish floor suspended above its parent hundreds of metres below. Mill Creek lies hidden from view from beyond the bush line opposite the Aspiring homestead, but it takes just minutes from the Aspiring hangars at Cattle Flat Station. Once inside, you're in a back country prison of rock and ice and snow, sealed off by steep, lacerated slopes. In the summer the Aspiring steers graze the valley floor, but they're mustered out well before the heaviest winter snows arrive. With their departure, a silence falls over the valley, save for the faint drawn-out cry of the mountain parrot. But in this inhospitable landscape there's another alpine dweller, a modern intruder high on the mountain slopes, indifferent to the savage cold.

Brought to New Zealand as a hunting resource, the goat-like chamois arrived in 1907, two males and six females, from the Alps of Austria and Switzerland, a gift from the Austrian Emperor Franz Josef II. Chamois are actually a type of antelope, and a truly elegant one at that. It's often considered the most beautiful of New Zealand's game animals, and it's quite at home in this mountain habitat. They move between bluffs with incredible agility, long legs springing sure-footedly off hooves made up of hard and soft surfaces, providing excellent grip over virtually any terrain. Chamois were first released in New Zealand beneath the precipices of Mount Cook, and today New Zealand remains the only place in the world where they've been successfully introduced.

With no natural predators, chamois soon spread unabated across the length of the Main Divide. They multiplied and encroached on the wilderness at a rate of six miles per year, much faster than their cohabitants, Himalayan tahr. Some people would even

With their distinctive hooked horns, chamois are regarded by all good keen hunters as a prized trophy of the Southern Alps.

come to describe their new home as a more favourable niche than their native home in Central Europe. They'll eat virtually anything that grows green in these mountains, and hunting is unrestricted. For Gary Walker and his son Mike, these hunting trips are what entice them to live here in the south. As father and son they've been up countless times — and it's in Mill Creek that Mike shot his first chamois as a young boy. Hunting is in their blood, and their fascination with the land and its creatures is as strong as ever.

'A lot of people have trouble with the fact that I'm a vet. That during the week I fix animals and then on the weekend I go out and kill 'em,' Gary says, as they set off through the dim light at the tail of the valley. 'But I was a keen hunter long before I decided to be a vet. I was brought up in a family very keen on hunting. My father was a keen hunter, and Mike's not too far behind. In his younger days Mike spent all of his time with me —

Gary and Mike Walker negotiating the icy edges of Mill Creek.

his mother actually encouraged it. Most weekends I'll use a firearm of some sort if I'm not committed to other things. And this is a hunter's paradise, Central Otago.'

Boulder-bashing through the creek, sliding along its cracked frozen edges with fists full of tussock, is slow and treacherous work. Gary leaps from a stone below the surface of the water and drives his stick into the frozen ground on the other side. Thick patches of ice form around his gaiters. 'It's no place to be ill-equipped. Bloody dangerous country if you get caught out so we'll need to get off the hill by dark. Once you get into this steep country and it's really cold the snow turns to sheet ice late in the day. And if you haven't got crampons with you, you'll have a hell of a time trying to get off the hill. It's hard to kick foot holes, and if you slip on sheet ice you're bloody history — gone. Some of the North Island boys aren't too good at clambering round in the steep. Hanging on by the skin of their teeth! You're pretty much on your own. And I can tell you now: if you camped in here tonight you'd know the very meaning of brass monkey.'

The expanse of the valley becomes clear after fighting through the watery narrows, and the sun soon blazes through the frozen tussock as it rises over the ridges. The landscape transforms. There's a silence but for the crunch of treaded soles.

Through their binoculars the Walkers see a disturbance on the slopes. The dark winter coats and the banded tan heads are an instant giveaway. A small herd of chamois, 400 metres up, bandits of the high country, grazing and bouncing across the tussock faces in the sun. They know we're here — no doubt they've been watching for some time — their exceedingly keen senses of sight and smell are so effective in these vast canyons. The Walkers watch in silence with a mix curiosity and admiration; observing, anticipating the kill, not something many hunters will dare to describe. It's not just the trophy or the bounty of meat that brings men to these hills. It's bearing witness to a wild animal in its natural environment, alone, mesmerized by the ease with which they move about their habitat.

Mike anchors his rifle against a flat rock. Unmoved by such a distant foe the chamois scale further down the slope towards him. There's a bated silence as Mike fine-tunes his calculations, zeroing in on the animal's kill zone. The release and recoil is sudden. A blue-tipped bullet pings through the air, a muffled snap echoes through the valley. The bullet spirals out of the barrel, travelling 312 metres in 1.1 seconds before the plastic wedge at its tip drives back into the bullet upon impact, mushrooming as the jacket peels away and exposes the lead core. The diameter doubles, making a huge wound channel, smashing and cutting through blood and bone as it drives through the chest. 'These bullets are designed to expand and kill,' Mike explains. 'Specifically designed to butcher things. You aim for the chest and if you accidentally go high, you hit the spine, which is fatal, too. Or if you go low, it's still normally a lung shot. Absolutely devastating, eh?'

This is the danger when guys accidentally shoot their mates. 'If you shoot anyone in the chest, they're history,' Gary continues. 'Anything from the waist up would be likely to be fatal. Except a shoulder wound, which might just blow off your arm. But then you're likely to bleed to death.' In order to get the best ballistics Mike hand-loads all his bullets, using all sorts of different projectiles and powders. 'You can customize them to suit your firearm and achieve slightly better velocity — and much better accuracy.'

With no natural predators the chamois immigrants flourished on the alpine vegetation of the South Island in the years after their arrival. In order to restrict their population, within just 25 years of its introduction, the government was forced to bring in a measure of control. The reduction in chamois numbers was part of a wider plan in the 1930s hatched in response to the devastating effects of deer on endemic flora and introduced pastures. It was the biggest control plan against large mammals the world had ever seen, and such was the ferocity of the crackdown on chamois that between 1936 and 1968 official control accounted for over 82,000 of the alpine antelope.

At the site of the kill Mike makes light work of slicing through the soft underbelly and gutting the animal. 'I've never seen anyone when I've been up in these valleys,' he says. Mike lived in the North Island for some time after attending Mount Aspiring College, a school with a highly respected outdoors programme, and has only just moved back to the area. For him it was an inevitable lifestyle decision, to come back south. 'It's just not the same up there, eh? I shot a few deer and did a bit of hunting up north but you walk for five hours through the bush and then you get to a sign that says: "Private property, no shooting". And you'd bump into about thirty people along the way.' Mike makes an incision in the chamois' hind leg, between the bone and tendon, and throws it over his shoulders. Deep in the valley below, Gary has put the billies on — there's boil-in-the-bag tucker and hot soup to be had.

Despite the carelessness surrounding the introduction of chamois to the Southern Alps, and the lack of a contemporary national management programme, they're now an accepted part of New Zealand's wild fauna. The Department of Conservation considers the eradication of chamois in New Zealand unrealistic — the European chamois is here to stay. There is a proud and active recreational hunting community in New Zealand with its own culture around the alpine pursuit of chamois and tahr. It's now to everyone's benefit that this culture thrives, not least New Zealand's exploited native flora and fauna. It's also these relationships with wild animals that have helped forge a deep respect for the land here, between mates and family alike. For the Walkers it's also about living off the land, and the appeal of living sustainably. They would never shoot more than they need, and it's not about profiting, showmanship or rivalry, it's about the landscape, delighting in nature, and continuing a heritage, something that rings true for all those who operate in the Matukituki Valley.

Gary Walker.

The chamois lies still in the snow by the riverbank as the familiar echo of the helicopter approaches in the valley. The sun is disappearing, a new freeze on its way — 'time to get off the hill'. The chamois shot at Mill Creek is bundled in the stowage compartment beneath the helicopter. When the Walkers get back to Wanaka it will be hung up for three days before Mike removes the back steaks and then uses the remaining meat for his salami recipe, which also incorporates freshly culled duck, deer and hare. They are all minced together and mixed with garlic, Cajun seasoning and dry salami mix. The meat is left to stand for a minimum of two hours, and from there it is pushed into large sausage skins and tied off, before it's put into a smokehouse, left to cool, and then is ready to eat — waste not, want not.

Growing up, the Aspinall children were used to the crack of the hunting rifle in the valley. Indeed John remembered shooting his first stag at just 12 years old. For the three brothers, John, Willie and Christopher, the wilderness abounded in all directions. 'In the summertime we would go fishing or hunting all the time, as you would only have to walk across the flat and you would usually see a deer,' Willie recalls. 'But usually we would wait until someone was planning to go to Wanaka before shooting anything. The tails from the deer were worth ten shillings, bought by an old Chinaman. Back then a deer added up to quite a bit of pocket money, even a hare was

Mill Creek.

about four shillings, and three shillings would buy about fifty rounds of ammunition.

'We used to wander a fair way sometimes. Go and camp up the river and stay the night. John would sometimes take the horses up the valley and camp at the flats, and any deer he shot he would put on the horses and bring back. We heard stories of hunters floating deer down the river, but we didn't have much luck. We worked out that they got an old tyre tube and stuffed it inside the deer to keep it afloat.'

The Matukituki Valley has a prestigious place in the history of deer hunting. Much of the Aspiring region is now comparatively free of deer, to the chagrin of the recreational hunter, but in the early years the valley produced some of the most impressive trophies ever seen. Like the first runholders to the area, the deer's heritage was in the Highlands of Scotland. In 1871 nine red deer calves from Invermark were released by the Otago Acclimatisation Society, an action some likened to opening the door of a china shop to a bull. There were also three releases at Hawea Flat, in 1891, 1895 and 1900, which became the basis for the large herds that were soon to appear over the ridges. They were at first protected, and remained almost undisturbed in the mountains, soon to produce an even finer stock than their ancestors in Scotland.

In the 1920s and '30s, the Aspinalls recorded herds up to 300 large, eating much of the station's palatable vegetation. 'It was nothing to see 200 or more on the flats in

Mike Walker.

the evening and large numbers above the bush line,' recalled Jerry. 'One fellow later told me that he had counted a thousand deer going out of the head of Mill Creek. That is an awful lot of the deer.' The main mobs of hinds were in the Minaret, Mill Creek and Cattle Face areas, while many of the stags wintered in the West Matukituki and along the ridges above Shotover Face. For a time, before the virgin vegetation was completely cleaned out, Jerry would tell visitors that Mill and McGills creeks made up the best head-hunting country in New Zealand. But with the uncontrolled breeding, inbreeding and food shortages, the quality of the progeny rapidly faded.

Culling of the large deer herds spreading throughout the high country had begun in earnest by the Otago Acclimatisation Society in the early 1900s. Deer were causing severe damage to pastures and alpine vegetation, and erosion became a serious consequence. Protection of the noble British game animal was removed from 1923, and soon the policy changed over from one of immunity to complete extermination. The Wildlife Branch of New Zealand's Department of Internal Affairs took control of the deer menace between 1931 and 1956, during which time an estimated population of between 1.4 million and 3 million was shot. The Noxious Animals Act of 1956 declared all deer, tahr, chamois and wild goats to be pests, and the New Zealand Forest Service, the forerunner of the Department of Conservation and the New Zealand Forestry Corporation, took over the responsibility for the cleansing, focusing on areas of critical importance like the Matukituki Valley. Between 1955 and 1958 alone, 9000 deer were shot on Mt Aspiring Station, and for many years before and after the Aspinalls provided crucial support for government deer-stalkers and recreational hunters alike, lending out station hacks to carry packs, rifles and stag heads. They'd also happily point them in the right direction.

Speaking with Philip Holden in the early 1990s for his classic book *Station Country*, John Aspinall reflected on the days of the great deer herds. 'Well, you'd see the deer every day when you were out working. They were a part of the everyday scene. You'd see, oh, thirty, forty, perhaps as many as seventy. It was common to see stags on our best winter blocks; they knew where the best, sweetest country was. I can recall seeing ninety once. Dad used to organize a drive every autumn, after we'd mustered out the sheep. He'd have perhaps fifteen shooters spread out in, say, a big basin, so that they'd cover all the main routes they'd use. They'd get two hundred, no trouble.'

The Matukituki Valley is also the pioneering country of the pilots, shooters and gutters of the deer wars, a remarkable passage of South Island history — telling of daring gunships sweeping across the Alps in the 1960s and 1970s. Previously, deer carcasses falling to the barrels of the government cullers lay where they were shot. But in October 1963 the 'a-ha' moment came when Sir Tim Wallis, 'Hurricane Tim',

Rob Roy Stream, a tributary of the West Matukituki.

hired a helicopter to recover deer carcasses from McGills Creek. Under Tim's direction a small group of shooters climbed up along the cattle tracks at Mt Aspiring Station to Mill Creek, scaling the ridge to McGills. Meanwhile a helicopter chased a mob of between 400 and 600 deer towards the shooting party. Between them they shot 300 deer, and although the helicopter couldn't recover them all, the experiment made a small profit, which was all the incentive needed to turn the venison industry on its head. Over the next two decades, shooting from the skids and hanging from strops, working from before dawn until after dark, crews of deer hunters began retrieving tallies of up to 200 per day, creating a multi-million dollar international export market.

Mike Walker with chamois.

The avian wolf

At the same time Jack and Jerry were battling to take control of the land overrun by rabbits and deer, another threat was descending with just as much consequence on the viability of farming in the valley. The story of the kea in the high country is one of the great tragedies of European colonization, and the future of this most remarkable parrot remains cast in a shadow of doubt.

During the last great ice age the kea, named by Maori on account of its distinctive drawn-out cry, developed a highly inquisitive nature. It was a mechanism for survival, a vital instinct in the search for food in a harsh alpine environment. Today the kea is widely regarded as the world's smartest bird, with a level of intelligence said to rival some primates. It has a particularly good memory, highly opportunistic tendencies, a mischievous personality and a beak like an ice-pick. For millions of years these parrots, endemic to the South Island, had the high ground to themselves. But the introduced species which spread unabated, particularly the large deer herds, pillaged the alpine vegetation kea were known to forage. The kea's habitats were quickly compromised, and the search for food became even more desperate through the long winters.

With their opportunistic tendencies in sync, it wasn't long before large flocks of kea started turning their attention to the livestock on the hills, tearing holes in their backs, goading them off cliffs and feeding on the carcasses. Equally desperate, farmers — backed up by the government — were quick to respond. Between 1898 and 1929 bounties were paid on an estimated 54,000 kea, and the battle continued for the next 40 years, a heartbreaking development for an endearing native bird.

Kea were a regular sight at the old homestead. 'Every now and again a big flock of keas would come and hang around the house for a week or two at a time before disappearing again,' Julia Aspinall remembers. 'And during that period, man, were they mischievous! They got up to some incredible antics. If they found a rag in the backyard they would have a tug of war, acting like a pair of kids, cackling, giggling, yahooing and somersaulting. They also liked to have races in the grooves of the corrugated iron roof, and then they would get to the spouting and sometimes hang upside down and look in through the kitchen window, watching what you were doing, their head on one side so they could see out of a beady little eye. If you were coming home or leaving with the tractor they would follow it in escort for about a kilometre.

'Dad absolutely loved them. He was totally intrigued by them, and the last thing he ever wanted to do was shoot any. But he always had his suspicions. One night he went out and stayed on the hill to watch what they were doing. They had started chasing sheep over bluffs. He could see what was going on — there were ringleader keas leading this bad behaviour. He also saw sheep coming in with big holes in their backs. The keas were sitting on their backs and eating through to where the kidney fat was. They were putting the stock through absolute agony. He would have been totally torn, but it was his and his family's livelihood at stake.'

A kea beneath Rob Roy Peak.

When growing up, Jerry had heard his father Jack talking with neighbours about kea and sheep carcasses. But as a young boy he hadn't realized the extent of the damage. When Jack died in 1942, a 20-year-old Jerry took over the station duties, and the kea soon had his attention. 'During the months of September and October I would find well-conditioned ewes dead on the flats, often with small lambs, even twins, starving alongside them. Some were down as far as the car park at the end of the Mt Aspiring road out in front of Raspberry Hut, from the door of which sometimes fifteen sheep carcasses could be counted.

'After seeing scores of dead sheep with blood-tinged froth at the nose, or dead at the foot of bluffs, I naturally became very suspicious, then firmly convinced. Close inspection invariably disclosed a small wound on the sheep's back. At shearing time many animals which had luckily escaped the blood poisoning infection came in with scars, some quite large, on their backs. Later, after I had inoculated the whole flock, ewes and hoggets, with hefty doses of penicillin more survivors started coming into the yards, with larger back wounds, often maggot-infested. Having a liking for the bird myself it took some time for me to realize what a cruel and ruthless killer he can be, and to harden my heart against him, and his undoubted charms.'

Jerry's usual procedure during the winter was to study the weather reports and pick what looked like being a fine night with a near full moon. 'After lunch, I would climb the hills where my sheep were wintering, with rifle, binoculars, sleeping bag, food, plenty of warm clothes, a good torch, new batteries and a spare bulb. I always carried my trusty hill-stick, a well-seasoned and shaved manuka pole some six feet long. It served as a third leg while traversing slopes or descending with a thirty to seventy pound pack on my back. It was also invaluable for testing the water depth before fording a discoloured stream, and probing the thickness of the snow and checking the level of the terrain before taking the next step.

'Once up the hills around the 2500 to 3000 feet level I would scan the slopes for carcasses, or hawks and seagulls circling, which would indicate the presence of animal remains. From sunset until it got too dark to see, I would try to plot the keas flying in from up, down or across the valley and to locate where they were feeding or killing. Some nights would be uneventful, with no harm from the birds. Other nights were busy ones. These expeditions meant tramping the frozen, snow-covered tussock slopes, trying to pick out sheep tracks, and avoid falling over bluffs, in moonlight or in the dark. It could be ten or even eleven o'clock before I got back to the shelter of the Cascade or Raspberry huts.

'One moonlit night I still well remember. It was so cold that as I sat in front of a roaring fire in the Cascade Hut, I had to break the ice every time I dipped water out of a bucket close behind me. I shudder now when I think of the consequences of a sprained ankle or a broken leg. In August 1948 I had been in Dunedin for a fortnight's holiday, the usual annual break from the station routine. On my return I decided that a look up the valley was the first priority. At ten o'clock in the morning I saw and heard five keas fly across the valley from below Sharks Tooth Peak, high above the Wishbone Falls. This caused apprehension, so I followed a ridge up to snow tussock level and found several sheep carcasses; some were only wool and bones. Further on I found a half-eaten carcass, so I positioned myself a few feet away in the tussocks. By two hours after nightfall I had shot thirty-two of the keas which came to feed on the carcass.'

Jerry Aspinall ran Mt Aspiring Station first with his mother and sister, then his wife and four children, from 1942 to 1977. His war against the kea on sheep country spanned from 1942 to 1970. In the years that followed, his son John found no further evidence of kea attacks. The Aspinalls concluded that, with the reduction in size of the large deer herds in the 1960s and '70s, the kea were returning to a diet of alpine vegetation, in particular the juicy winter berries of *Coprosma serrulata*. It was also in the 1970s that all bounties on kea were lifted with the formation of national parks. Today the Department of Conservation estimates there are between 1000 and 5000 birds remaining in the wild. They have been given the status 'nationally endangered'.

The dog kennels at Mt Aspiring Station

The road toward Mount Aspiring.

Cascade Creek, West Matukituki Valley.

Opposite: A possum at Mt Aspiring Station.

Public enemies

Mount Aspiring National Park is now within an area called Te Wahipounamu, South West New Zealand UNESCO World Heritage Area, a global concept placing protected status on areas that are so valuable, they surely concern all people. Te Wahipounamu is 26,000 square kilometres, made up of Fiordland, Westland, Aoraki/Mount Cook and Mount Aspiring national parks. The natural criteria for the world heritage rating requires areas to have, among other things, superlative natural phenomena, areas of exceptional natural beauty and aesthetic importance; outstanding examples representing the major stages of earth's history; and those which contain the most important and significant natural habitats for *in situ* conservation of biological diversity. The decision to award the rating was also based on the thought that the area contains some of the best modern representations of the original flora and fauna present in Gondwana, the southern supercontinent of which New Zealand was a part 510 to 252 million years ago.

For the Aspinalls growing up at Aspiring the sounds of the forest were always near. Around the old homestead New Zealand pigeons would feed in great numbers on small round sponges growing on the silver beech trees and spring shoots on the crack willows; a welcome break in the rain would always bring the familiar bell-like tune of the bellbird; while the insect-eating fantails, tomtits and riflemen patrolled the branches and trunks above the ferns and mosses of the beech forest margins. High above, native falcons crested the valley winds, and at night the solitary cry of New Zealand's surviving native owl, the morepork, haunted the mountainside. On the flats, the river-nesting birds — pairs of paradise shelducks, spur-winged plovers and oystercatchers — made up the everyday scene.

Above the tree line, at about 1100 metres, subalpine shrubland gives way to the alpine tussocks where large endemic grasshoppers feed after the snowmelt, and the long-legged weta lurk under the broken rock and alpine screes. Above them live the alpine birds, the kea, who regularly visit the valley floor with their meddlesome beaks. In all, 45 native bird species have been recorded in the valley, but their threats are many, and today none is without enemies.

Since 1920 the Aspinalls have witnessed the rapid spread of alien predators in the Matukituki, and there has always been an unwritten law protecting the environment alongside day-to-day farming operations. From an early age Jerry Aspinall considered himself an environmentalist, an ornithologist and a botanist, and so by the time a review of the Aspiring pastoral lease came up in the 1960s, where others might have chosen to slash, burn and make way for new pastures, Jerry made a bold decision

Florence Gaud setting off on the stoat-trapping line between Aspiring Hut and Pearl Flat.

to help secure the future of the native environment. In 1957 Mt Aspiring Station voluntarily surrendered most of run number 468 to the Crown, some 20,235 hectares. This area helped to form the basis of the provisional Mount Aspiring National Park, which was gazetted in 1964. Jerry then also became one of the nine inaugural members of the semi-autonomous park board, on which he served for many years to ensure the interests of the land and its endemic ecosystems were preserved for future generations.

The narrow channel leading up Matukituki Valley into Mount Aspiring National Park can be a disheartening place in the winter. As the skies close in with fits of lightning around Aspiring Hut near the head of the valley, Department of Conservation wardens Flo Gaud and Kerie Uren remain undeterred, setting off along the stoat-trapping lines of the West Matukituki. There are 52 traps in the area, and it forms a significant programme for the Department of Conservation Wanaka branch. In the summer a warden is resident at the hut all season, and will check the stoat lines every three weeks. But in the winter Flo and Kerie will come up over the Aspinalls' four-wheel drive track every six weeks to check the traps and continue work on programmes to revitalize the forest's fauna. They're also on the lookout for one of New Zealand's ancient forest birds, the South Island robin or kakariwai. It's

South Island robin. *Image courtesy of Florence Gaud.*

one of several birds that have been missing from the Matukituki in recent years.

In the nineteenth century, trampers and explorers were overawed by the abundance of forest life in the Matukituki, but since the introduction and rapid spread of predators the chorus of the endemic forest birds is a fragment of its former self. When James Hector came through the valley in the 1860s he noted weka as being 'extraordinarily numerous', 'trees in the forest literally thick with kaka', and an 'inquisitive little robin, so friendly as to prefer a perch on your knee or head'. Hector also noted a visit by a South Island kokako, a wattlebird declared extinct in 2007.

Over the decades trampers would witness the rapid decline of weka, kaka, brown kiwi, blue duck and yellowhead to the point of nonexistence. Still, in recent years there have been some positives to take away from the ever-changing story of conservation in the back country.

In 2008, over 30 years after their disappearance from the Matukituki, 22 South Island robins were flown in by helicopter from the Dart Valley and released in the red beech forest behind Aspiring Hut. Since then DOC rangers have noticed the numbers increasing. Having been associated with the Mount Aspiring National Park for 40 years, the increase in birdlife in this pocket of the Matukituki is something retired DOC biodiversity manager and ranger Stu Thorne is particularly proud of. 'Over the years we've noticed a big difference in the birdlife up there. As valleys go it's still not great, but it's a lot better than it was. It was in a very degraded state. I remember tramping up there a long time ago and seeing many robins, but all of a sudden they just disappeared — there were just too many predators.

Paul Blackgrove of Waimate.

ZF3325

Clockwise from bottom left: A camper van parked at the Raspberry Creek car park; one of Paul Blackgrove's possum traps; silver beech tree on the West Matukituki Valley track; a wood pigeon in a willow by the West Matukituki River.

'The predator numbers would vary. Sometimes you would get the feeling there was nothing around at all and other times you thought you would never get on top of them — wildcats, rats, hedgehogs, stoats and possums. Stoats in particular, they're just little killing machines. They kill not only for food but for fun, and no one hunts them, so they have free rein. Plus, they're such an adaptable and surviving mammal that it's hard to make any impression on their population. When the young stoats are born the male stoat impregnates the females straight away. So when those young stoats mature they're already pregnant. It's incredible.'

The West Matukituki headwaters are now considered a high biodiversity area and a priority for DOC ground control, but stoats, possums and rats are found throughout the national park and its fringes. To the heartache of DOC workers their control over wide areas is impractical given current resources and technology. 'The best thing for stoats of course is 1080,' says Stu. 'The Routeburn was 1080'd three years ago, and it made a huge difference. It got rid of most of the possums and stoats and it's only now after three years that the numbers are building up again. In the Matuki we've never used 1080. We've used some poisons — cyanide, 1080 pellets — but not an aerial drop.

'The problem is DOC really have to justify spending the money. If there was a big population of mohua [yellowhead] or some sort of endangered bird up there they would definitely do something, but there's not.' Not yet anyway. Stretched resources have always been a problem for the department, and the success of noxious animal control has often hinged on the cooperation of adjoining runholders to assist and help create a buffer zone.

The Aspinalls are aware of the challenges facing the native fauna and flora in the valley better than most, and they've always believed in taking matters into their own hands, as well as forming a united front. In more recent years the Department of

Conservation have had several pest control programmes running on the station. One they have had significant success with is the ongoing programme to control goats from spreading into the Matukituki via the station boundaries. DOC staff undertaking the control have always worked with the Aspinalls to run the programme as one, often agreed on a handshake, regardless of what the land status is.

Goats were originally introduced to the region during the gold rushes as food and as a crude way of clearing land for agriculture. If given the opportunity, goats will eat bark, grass and everything in between. In two winter campaigns alone three Forest Service men killed 6343 goats in the Shotover watershed. The total up until that point had been some 100,000 goats, but there weren't the resources to follow them from the Shotover into the Matukituki. At the time Jerry Aspinall was on the noxious animals committee as a representative from Federated Farmers. He was an outspoken leader on the issue. 'I would suggest, even entreat, every runholder, shooter or person interested in the alpine country to make every effort to eradicate goats — we are willing to assist any person.'

Throughout the programme Jerry's station hands on the top mustering beats along the Shotover Faces were always armed with a rifle and encouraged to be vigilant. By keeping the boundary secure the goat problem was largely contained. Around the same time Jerry appeared in a photo with his son John, reporting he had shot the first Himalayan tahr in the Wanaka district. Tahr were released in New Zealand three years before chamois, and their New Zealand population remains the only significant wild tahr herd outside the Himalayas. Mt Aspiring Station became instrumental in the 1960s to help create a tahr-free area, which now exists as a southern exclusion zone blanketing an area from the Shotover to the Haast River.

That Jerry was so ready to use his human resources in tandem with DOC came down to having already seen the effects of pests left to propagate without a sustained control programme. For generations of high country farmers public enemy number one was, and still is, in large swathes of the country, the common European rabbit. Unlike other stations, the impact of rabbits at Aspiring today is negligible, and the Aspinalls plan to keep it that way, but it wasn't always so. Rabbits in New Zealand still thrive in their preferred habitats of semi-arid areas of the Mackenzie Basin and Central Otago, but for much of the twentieth century they also had a strong foothold in the wetter valleys of the Alps.

When Jack took over the lease from the Macphersons in the 1920s, the rabbit problem was severe. As soon as Jerry was old enough to set traps without catching his fingers it became his first responsibility outside correspondence schooling. The battle against rabbits went on unabated throughout Jack's lifetime running the station, and when he died in January 1942, Jerry, his mother Amy and sister Pat were left

One of the Department of Conservation's 52 stoat traps between Cascade Hut and Pearl Flat in the Matukituki Valley.

to continue the fight. Although the rabbit skin and carcass trade was on the rise, the Aspinalls could barely keep up with the rate of natural increase, and in desperation Jerry soon turned to poison. But first 'I had to learn the finer points of using baits and poison without poisoning myself. Unfortunately, I lost several good mustering dogs.' Jerry's mother Amy and sister Pat also helped when and where they could. On one occasion they assisted to pick up some 350 dead rabbits in a single outing, riding back on horseback 10 miles in a strong nor'west gale.

'Skinning and burying the carcasses followed picking up,' said Jerry. 'I became quite proficient at skinning and at times could do up to a hundred per hour in reasonable conditions. Frozen carcasses and cold wet weather slowed me down, and my back was sore by the 300 mark.' By the end of the 1940s help came from above as fixed-wing aircraft began large-scale 1080 poisoning programmes in the inaccessible back country. From that moment on stock numbers began to increase, along with wool and carcass weights.

Long gone are the rabbit plagues of yesteryear, but even in recent times the Aspinalls remain ever-watchful. Night-shooting used to be a highly anticipated annual event, according to Sue. 'There's a group who used to come for three nights in the winter and would get a lot of possums and hares, but not as many rabbits. Even so,

John always liked to keep tallies. And even if we were at home and I ever saw a rabbit on the lawn, I'd say, "John ...," and he'd rush off and get his gun.'

The dark days of kea attacking sheep in the high country might be over, but the future of New Zealand's biggest avian personality is still under threat, their population stagnating at best. 'It's a bit of a worry really,' says Stu Thorne. 'Some scientists think there has been a lot of kea deaths as a result of lead poisoning, particularly around Arthur's Pass. But we got ours tested and there was no sign of any lead poisoning in their blood at all. We don't know; it's just one of those things. What I think has happened is the stoats have established themselves on higher ground. When they first arrived in this area they mainly kept below the bush line, but now we're finding them in the alpine country. I have no evidence to substantiate this, but I've certainly seen them up that high. They're probably going into the kea nests — and same with the falcon nests — dealing to whatever they find.'

The mystery of the stagnating population of kea is the latest episode of an already long and prickly history of the mountain parrot. The future of this high country symbol will in no small part depend on its ability to outwit its predators. Whether or not the kea can pull itself back from the brink of extinction will also depend upon the resourcefulness of the high country community to bring pests down from the alpine zones.

In the twenty-first century, vying for the number one most-wanted pest by both the conservation estate and high country farmers is the Australian brushtail possum. 'Possums are just as bad as stoats for killing off native wildlife,' says DOC's Stu Thorne. 'They climb the trees, get into the eggs or eat the young. In the earlier days, thirty years ago, there never used to be a big problem with them because the price of fur was so high. You would get trappers coming in every winter, staying for weeks and months on end, and they would clean everything out. Now, although it's starting to come back because they're mixing it with the merino, it's still not as profitable as it was before.'

Between 1837 and 1875 there were 15 known releases of the Australian brushtail possum between Auckland and Southland based on the potential for sport and fur in what was to become one of New Zealand's greatest ecological disasters. Recent estimates suggest there are up to 70 million possums in New Zealand, consuming up to 22,000 tonnes of vegetation every day, and spreading bovine tuberculosis and other diseases to domestic animals. Since the 1990s possum fur prices have been low, forcing trappers and hunters out of the industry. Even so, there are still a few hearty souls trapping good numbers around the fringes of the national parks. The Aspinalls have always encouraged hunting and trapping on the station, freeing up Raspberry Hut for such purposes.

Paul Blackgrove at Raspberry Hut.

Making quick work between possum traps.
Opposite: Warm-plucking a possum.

Paul Blackgrove from Waimate is in his ninth season possuming at Aspiring. He spends eight weeks at the start of winter living at Raspberry Hut. 'No one knows how long it's been here, probably since the 1920s,' says Paul, stoking the fireplace as the rain begins to lash the windows. 'But it's nice and cosy.' Paul is a freezing worker by trade, a lamb-boner, and a proud one at that, but every chance he gets he'll drive up to the environment he loves the most. 'I think I'm the oldest one at the works. It's pretty tough going but if you keep yourself fit you can do the job. But I've always been an outdoor sort of a person. Most people when they get eight weeks off will go for a holiday, but I prefer to come up here because I enjoy doing the possuming. I don't know about the isolation, I'm still getting used to that!' It isn't a glamorous existence, although the scenery certainly helps, and you can still make a buck if you're fit, have the right equipment and prepare for the cold.

'I've always been known to have clean and dry fur,' Paul says, pinching off tiny strands of fur from his fingertips. 'Some days you get it wet, but you just put it in the mutton bag and leave it on the porch where it's quite warm. That's yesterday's effort,' he says, pointing to a white bag on the wood pile. 'There's a couple of kilos there. It wasn't a great day, but then I'm not here to break any records!' Paul traps the possums with a galvanized leg-hold Duke trap. 'You nail the chain to the tree and they just come along and put their feet in the trap and then bang! It doesn't hurt their feet too much and you very rarely lose things out of them. I have a hundred of these, but I don't always put a hundred out. But by the time you go around sixty or seventy traps that's a decent day.'

WAIMATE

Helicopter at Mill Creek.

Each morning Paul sets off on a four-wheel drive quad bike from Raspberry Hut, checking his trap lines, locating them by the small pink ribbons he ties on branches near the trap the day before. He'll spend the first week or so along the gullies and patches of bush between Raspberry Creek and the homestead, before setting off into the east branch of the Matukituki. It's a fairly straightforward process, and if you ask him what his preferred tools of the trade are, he'll only have to raise his trusty steel hammer. By grabbing the possum's tail and striking it hard enough between the ears, the hammer will stun the possum instantly. Then, another strike with the possum's head positioned on a nearby rock will crush its skull.

The best time to trap possums for fur is with the onset of winter, when the furs are thickening. 'It has to be a certain length, you see,' says Paul, resetting the trap and reapplying the sugary bait. 'You can either machine-pluck or hand-pluck it. If you poison them, they'll be cold in the morning, so you'd have to use a plucking machine, a bit like a duck-plucker. A lot of people poison them, but John wasn't as keen on that, and I'm quite happy trapping and hot-plucking all mine, plus you will clean them out better trapping than with poison because they soon become poison-shy. As soon as you knock them on the head you have to pluck them within about five minutes. The fur comes out quite easily. The manufacturers prefer them hand-plucked because you're not breaking the fur off and it's also slightly longer. I've even heard that the wee bit that goes into the skin of the possum when it comes out helps hold the fur into the merino when it's mixed together and spun.

'That fur there goes to a Waimate knitwear manufacturer, and he sends it down to Milton and has it dyed and blended, 60 per cent merino, 40 per cent possum fibre. Then he gets the yarn back and he knits it into jumpers, gloves and hats — it makes garments beautiful and soft. There are quite a few buyers in New Zealand, but apart from that everything else will go to China.'

The prices for possum fur are down a bit this year at around $100 to $120 per kilo, but Paul thinks he'll probably get about $135 per kilo. 'So I suppose the money's not too bad,' he says. 'It's such a great natural product, and this is the only country you can get it!' Paul usually aims to get around 1000 to 1200 possums a year off Aspiring, but last year he got a most satisfying 1400. It's not as profitable as it used to be, and at times it's a solitary, wet and back-breaking existence. But he can rest assured he's also playing a vital role in reducing the impact of the 'Kiwi bear' on the native wildlife population, which would otherwise go largely unchecked around these park margins.

As management of the station passed from father to son in the 1970s, so too did the core values of land protection from invasive species. But with the decline of deer, rabbits and kea, invaders of a less obvious but just as prolific kind were appearing from beneath. John Aspinall had foreseen one of the biggest challenges facing the high country in decades from an early stage — the control of invasive weeds like wilding conifers, gorse, broom, briar, ragwort and herbs of the *Hieracium* genus. In particular, John dedicated much of his last years to setting up the Hieracium Control Trust, a farmer-led initiative to better understand and control the prolific European invader, commonly known as hawkweed, a relative of the dandelion.

Today, hieracium is still strangling the tussocklands of the high country in areas of low-intensity grazing, and two species in particular, mouse-ear and king devil, have become the most abundant plants in the tussock country. The control trust has been working with the Ministry of Agriculture and Forestry's Sustainable Farming Fund and Landcare Research to introduce several insect species that attack hieracium, but the effectiveness of these introductions will not be known for several years.

In the 1980s John gave up playing rugby to devote more of his time to farming politics, and much of this he pledged to land protection. At one stage John was the only farmer on the Otago Conservation Board, where he was often outvoted,

Bridge to the Rob Roy walk. *Image courtesy of Kieran Scott.*

but nonetheless presented arguments hard-line conservationists might never have considered otherwise, further bridging the divide between neighbours. 'Why did he do it?' asks Paul Hellebrekers, DOC Wanaka area manager. 'I think he just had a genuine love of the land and anything special within that land. He just had a really strong affiliation with the country where he lived and brought up his family, and he wanted to see it managed in a way that was sustainable the best he could, protecting those values of the property he wasn't farming. The land wasn't being overgrazed or mismanaged, so he was clearly trying to farm within the limits of the land.'

Peter Taylor worked at Aspiring as a 19-year-old under Jerry Aspinall in 1972, after coming off an intensive cropping farm in Ashburton. To this day it remains 'easily one of the best jobs I ever had. No question. It was the only job I ever regretted leaving. I can just about quote you what I wrote in the Aspiring visitor's book when I left. My words to Jerry and John were "Please don't change this too much, because it's a treasure." And I'd still give them that message now.' For Peter it was also a place and time that influenced the rest of his career. 'Jerry taught me the beginnings of understanding the relationship between farming and the environment, and how those two can work in relative harmony — it was the greatest thing I learnt from him.'

After his time at Aspiring Peter ended up working for the New Zealand Wildlife Service for 13 years, followed by 27 years at Fish and Game, and he makes his opinions on some farming practices well known. 'How do you squander it? By destroying it. Even since the 1970s I've seen farmers destroy a huge amount of New Zealand's biodiversity. They have drained wetlands and converted them to pasture, cleared bush remnants that should have been left alone, and have created serious water-quality issues. That wasn't Jerry, or John; money wasn't their driving force and they didn't squander what they had been privileged to work with. High country farmers in New Zealand have tended to be very good at understanding how they can survive from one year to the next, and have probably very astutely avoided what could be overexploitation of the land.'

Above all John Aspinall believed it was the land manager's fundamental duty to assist the capacity of the land and its surrounding environment to support life, and to maintain acceptable standards of soil structure, nutrient levels, micro-fauna, water and air quality. Within these standards, John also believed in sustaining the inherent values of native conservation, recreation and, not least, preserving history and heritage. He believed all these ingredients were inseparable from the high country's capacity to support life, and the farm business unit had a duty to keep it that way. John practised what he preached: the stock numbers at Aspiring have always been kept on the level, and you won't see large mobs of animals creating high volumes of waste, or overgrazing erosion-prone land.

It's a fundamental philosophy for the Aspinalls, something they all carry with them, wherever they live, as John and Sue's daughter Catie, now living in Ireland, would remind you. 'People will talk about how farmers ruin the environment, but if this is your livelihood, the greatest thing you own and what you want to pass down through the family, then you're going to look after it. It's always been my view that farmers are in it for the long haul. Most farmers in a high country environment aren't even in it to make money — because they don't — they're in it because they love it and the livelihood it can offer them. You still take the good years when you get them, and you do what you can to improve the productivity, but it's got to be sustainable, because if it's not sustainable, then you're just wasting your time.'

John and Sue's approach to farming in the high country was recognized when they became the supreme winner of the Otago Ballance Farm Environment Awards in 2006. The key objective of the award was to display to farmers that profitability need not compromise environmental values. Indeed, past winners of the award have shown that the environment can be both restored and enhanced under profitable farming systems.

Whare Kea chalet. *Image courtesy of Whare Kea.*

The swing bridge marking the entrance into the Matukituki from the Rob Roy track, one of New Zealand's most popular day walks.

At the gates of heaven on earth

When run number 468 was transferred to the conservation estate in the 1960s it made little difference to the way Mt Aspiring Station operated. The family at its helm had always been mindful of keeping a balance between conservation and their own livelihood. But one of the biggest changes in the decades that followed was the prominence of the area on the tourism map. The influx of 'loopies' became further pronounced with the rise of Wanaka as a tourism hub on the back of the ski industry in the 1970s. But rather than react to the potential threats to the management of their stock, the Aspinalls continued to encourage access, in all its shapes and forms, and they also became important spokespeople for the farming collective on land access issues.

When the station was passed down to John Aspinall the ethos of the two generations before him remained strong. On any other station, Paul Hellebrekers, DOC Wanaka area manager, could have had a nettlesome battle on his hands. But to the contrary, Paul and John developed a unified force in both the eradication of noxious weeds and pests as well as public land access. Paul says: 'They were in an important position to allow it. It's literally the stepping stone to Mount Aspiring National Park, but they have always had the right to use their trespass provisions and deny all public access over their pastoral lease. I don't think the Aspinalls ever denied anyone. They have just worked out ways to farm around it. And the stock have clearly gotten used to it, too — it's evolved together very well.'

A 2009 estimate had 80,000 visitors pass over Mt Aspiring Station's land in a single year, few of whom would ever have known they were on private land. Aside from the odd gate left unlatched, there are very few problems with recreationists, and most also enjoy the presence of the affable Aspiring stock. 'I think a lot of people really enjoy just being able to walk through farmland,' says Catie Aspinall. 'A lot of people have said how amazing it is to walk up the valley while the cows just look at you and go back to their own business. They're not at all skittish. A lot of people have stopped and said how nice it is to see the animals up close. If you spend a lot of time in the city, animals might not be something you come into contact with a lot. Part of getting out of the city is to see animals in their own habitat. So that's as much a part of the experience for some people as being able to get up into the mountains far away from where anyone else is.' It takes a certain type of farmer to remain calm with 80,000 people walking among your prized beef cows or pregnant ewes in spring, but the Aspinalls have developed an unflappable demeanour much like their livestock. It also requires patience — patience with tourists, crowding in for photographs of mobs coming down the road, patience with camper vans stuck in the river, and patience with backpackers, running out of petrol.

Shared access has also remained a strong guiding force in the way the Aspinalls have

The Whare Kea chalet and Mount Aspiring. *Image courtesy of Whare Kea.*

managed their farm assets and powers of building consent. Aside from the back country hut at Raspberry Creek, there are a number of buildings that have been on the station land for some time. In their day, Jerry, John, Christopher, Willie and Randall Aspinall all attended Otago Boys' High School after correspondence schooling. The affiliation has remained strong, and the Aspinalls have, in return, provided thousands of Otago students with the broader outdoor education they themselves received growing up. It started when Jerry and Phyllis moved everything across the river to a new homestead at Glenfinnan.

'When we left the old house we didn't know what to do about it. You couldn't put a married couple there, because having endured the hard conditions there I wasn't going to worry about someone else having to put up with it. And we didn't want to just walk out, because we knew stray types would fell it board by board if it was just left. So after some thought we gave the use of it to Otago Boys' and Dunstan High School in Alexandra. I think it's about the best thing we've done. It's very precious to me, that bond.' Dunstan High School and Mount Aspiring College still use the old homestead site for outdoor education camps, but in 1974 Otago Boys' High School built a lodge around the corner in the West Matukituki. John Aspinall helped ferry materials across the river to the building site, and remained available to every school visit since.

Over 10,000 boys have spent time in the valley, many of whom will fondly

Otago Boys' High School lodge store.

Otago Boys' High School lodge, Matukituki Valley.

remember John and Sue's after-dinner talks on high country life. The lodge is described as a 'jewel in the Otago Boys' High School crown', and the boys leave with the outdoor skills of kayaking, abseiling and tramping — but most of all they leave with a deeper understanding of biology, geography and the balance of the land; generations of young men growing up with an attachment to the environment, an environment that will need their help and understanding for generations to come.

There's a building near the old station boundary which stands higher than any other for miles around. It's like a monument to all that John Aspinall stood for, the values of sharing the environment in a sustainable way. It stands on the Albert Burn Saddle at the end of what, until recent tenure review, was the boundary with the national park. It's a one-of-a-kind alpine gem, with views to Mount Cook on the horizon and Mount Aspiring to the west. The chalet was built by the Myer family of Melbourne in 2003, as an extension of the luxury lodge Whare Kea, on the banks of Lake Wanaka. Off the back of what has become the largest department store chain in Australia, the Myer family manage a broad investment portfolio of international ventures and philanthropic activities via the Sidney Myer Fund and the Myer Foundation.

Keen heliskier and confessed outdoors fanatic, Myer Foundation president Martyn Myer is the proprietor of the Whare Kea lodge and chalet. Martyn spends around

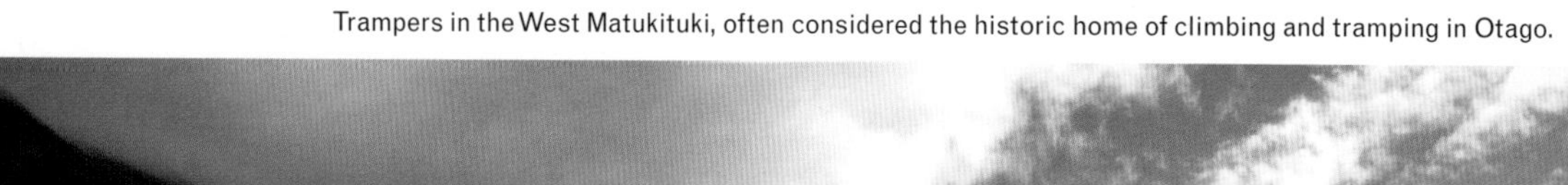

Trampers in the West Matukituki, often considered the historic home of climbing and tramping in Otago.

Fishing for trout, which are still seen in abundance in the West Matukituki since their introduction in the 1870s.

50 days a year in this part of the world with his wife, and he'll have you believe it is, quite simply, 'heaven on earth'. Ever since Martyn visited Wanaka in 1988 he'd had a daydream about building something at high altitude. 'What I wanted was something that was fairly unique,' he says. I had already stayed in some of the DOC huts, which are more orientated to provide access to one point or another. I wanted to create something in a unique location. It had to be remote, but obviously not in an avalanche path; you had to have beautiful views, sunshine all day and you had to be able to walk in and out. So it didn't take us long to sit down and say, well, there were only a couple of spots that met all those criteria. The ideal location just happened to be on the Aspiring lease, so I went and cold-called John and said, "I've got this crazy idea, what do you think?" Being the kind of bloke he was he could see the merit of the idea straight away.'

Generally accessed via helicopter from the front lawn of the Whare Kea lodge, the chalet is set in an alpine wilderness at some 1750 metres' altitude. There's been an emphasis on sustainability and sensitivity to the environment, while providing an unpretentious feel to the two bedrooms, living area and bathroom. 'We just collect water off the roof and sunlight for energy. We fly food in and the garbage out. That's

The swing bridge into the wilderness of the Rob Roy.

it. It's built in a very sustainable way. It's also built to last a very long time,' says Martyn. 'We designed it for 300 kilometre per hour winds. The highest we've had on the anemometer so far is 176 kilometres, but that's only been up a year and a half. I think we'll have 200 to 250, because of where it is in the saddle. In most mountain huts the strength has to be in the walls, so the windows must be very small. In the chalet all the strength is in the steel, so you can have floor to ceiling windows. That's unique for a mountain hut, certainly in New Zealand.'

If you choose, it's also a very solid day's walk out, which is 'not without its risk in those sorts of conditions,' Martyn continues. 'You have to know what you're doing up there, which is why we always send a fully qualified guide up. But to me that adds the edge; you learn how to work in the environment and manage the risk. That's one of the things that drives me. It's funny what then becomes important; so much of the crap in your life is just crap and really not important at all. My greatest pleasure is to take people to the area who haven't experienced it before. Because I think it's heaven on earth and for most people it changes their life. We've had the most sophisticated people you could meet up there, and they've said it's one of the most incredible experiences they've ever had.

'The philosophy is also about providing access to the mountains to people who wouldn't normally consider themselves capable. For example, I've had my niece who's in a wheelchair up there, and I've had my 85-year-old aunt up there. People just get blown away. You then end up helping to create a community that is concerned and passionate about looking after the mountains. John was a believer in the multi-tiered, graded-use pattern, and I am too. I think that's why he let so many people use his land.

His view was that the more people who could enjoy it the better. Provided he could still have his cattle!'

By the time Martyn Myer approached John to the build the Whare Kea chalet, he had already made his views on land access publicly well known. In a *Country Calendar* television programme episode that aired in the mid-'90s, John was highlighted as saying: 'I believe strongly in multiple use and I believe there is opportunity for farming, for tourism, for freedom recreation all to co-exist quite happily.' At the time he was chairman of the Federated Farmers High Country Committee. He was also a passionate conservationist, tramper, hunter and fisherman, in a better position than most to understand the way in which the high country could be made to work for everyone within the limits of the land, a philosophy he worked tirelessly for right up until his death.

'Someone once asked me if he ever sat down and relaxed,' Sue recalls. 'He did, but he always had his diary and recording books beside him wherever he went. It wasn't hard to see that John was a hard worker who gave his all to everything he became involved with.' The following list is not exhaustive, and it is included here only as a reminder of an impassioned being, someone who never sat back without knowing he'd done all he could for what he held dear at the gates of heaven. The list of contributions outside the farm gate began in the mid-1970s, almost as soon as he took over Aspiring from his father Jerry. It included local Young Farmers Groups, 1975 to 1982; lead negotiator on planning issues with the Lakes Landcare Group since 1992; the Otago Conservation Board from 1990 to 1998; Federated Farmers Otago section committee from the mid-1980s; Federated Farmers High Country Committee 1992 to 1999, the last three years as chairman; Federated Farmers National Board 1999 to 2005; spokesman for Federated Farmers Action Orange campaign; a member of the Biosecurity Ministerial Advisory Committee since 2004, the Walking Access Consultation Panel and the Walking Access Advisory Board, thereafter on the board of the Walking Access Commission since 2008, including chairman of the mapping committee since 2005; on the board of Hieracium Control Trust since 1993, including chairman since 1995; honoured with a significant achievement award by the Otago branch of the Institute of Agricultural Science in 1995; a member of the National Rural Fire Advisory Committee from 1999 to 2005, and Mid Dome Wilding Tree Trust since 2006; a member of land-based search and rescue; a member of the Queenstown Lakes 'Shaping the Future' Steering Committee 2011; and a trustee for Otago Boys' High School and Mount Aspiring Outdoor Education Trusts.

In the last 15 years of his life alone, John logged almost 12,000 hours devoted to off-farm committees, a third of his total working hours.

Epilogue

Tinged with sadness

John Aspinall in the spring of 2009. *Image courtesy of Kieran Scott.*

Rachal Aspinall reflects: 'I had sensed that I was going to lose my dad young. Dad was a fit guy that always looked after himself. But it's a fact of life, we live in a broken world, people get sick and they die and there's not much you can do about it. You just make the most of what you've got and carry on.' In October 2011 John Henry Aspinall of Mt Aspiring Station suffered a stroke and died in Dunedin Hospital in November after contracting an infection his blood disorder had been battling for some time. His funeral was attended by over 1000 people. His pallbearers included daughters Catie and Rachal, son Randall, brothers Willie and Christopher, and sister Julia. A guard of honour was provided by a class from Otago Boys' High School. Condolences poured in from every corner, from the New Zealand Federation of Freshwater Anglers to the Upper Clutha Rugby Club.

John was just 60 years old when he died and had an enormous contribution still to make to the high country. Yet he left knowing that he had done all he could to secure the future of his family and its affiliation with Mount Aspiring. Just four months before he died, Mt Aspiring Station completed tenure review, seven years after it entered the process. The outcome was that 7345 hectares of the station land was ceded to the public conservation estate, with the remaining 2309 hectares designated Aspinall freehold land. It might have come as a surprise to high country farmers, the alpine fraternity and recreationists alike, when the news of Aspiring's tenure review broke, not that it should have because in reality they had very little choice. Now that tenure review has been completed many of the access points to the national park entrances and the Matukituki Valley have been solidified as public easements, but very few people will notice a difference, at least in the short term.

Tenure review has been a hotly debated issue in the recent unfolding drama of New Zealand's high country. To give its back-story, in the South Island, early high country farming relied on Crown leasehold land, given the large and extensive nature of farming those areas. Much of the high country has remained leased since the 1850s in an effort to get runholders to invest their time and stock over vast areas of inhospitable mountain land. The leases were consolidated under the Land Act of 1948, which granted the land holders exclusive occupation rights, ownership of improvements and fixed rentals — but no right of freehold — in return for practising 'good husbandry'. In 1998 the government passed the Crown Pastoral Land Act, further consolidating the pastoral leases with entitlement to perpetual right of renewal and, crucially, a rent review every 11 years. The Act also established new grounds for good faith tenure-review bargaining, a system designed to cede freehold ownership of the most productive pastoral land to farmers in return for land with high recreation and inherent 'landscape' values to the conservation estate. Previously leaseholders couldn't put their land to more intensive use without consent, nor could they sell or subdivide (they could only sell the lease to farm). By freeholding, farmers could treat it like any other landowner. In 2002, 303 farming families still had pastoral leases in an area stretching along the mountains from Marlborough to Southland. By the middle of 2012, 83 of those had completed tenure review, 110 had entered into the process, while five properties had been purchased outright by the Crown for tens of millions of dollars.

As the news of Aspiring's completed tenure review spread, with his body slowly failing him, John Aspinall was quoted in the media as feeling relieved yet pained by the station's break-up. 'The Aspinall family are relieved to have achieved secure freehold tenure over the majority of the grazing land. However, this is tinged with sadness at losing the management responsibility for a large area of land which has been with our family for 91 years. We hope that the new managers feel as much passion for that land as we do.'

Although the process was theoretically voluntary, for John it appeared he was being made an offer he couldn't refuse. In a conversation with fellow search and rescue

volunteer and friend Phil Melchior, John said: 'If you opt out, the future looks very hazy. They can make it more difficult to manage pasture, put up rentals, and just make life harder. In the old days, when we talked about "amenities" we meant proximity to schools, doctors and shops. The landscape was just something that was there, no one ever tried to ascribe a monetary value to it.' For a time, it looked as though rents would be increased based on amenity values such as lake and mountain views, but after the high-profile Minaret Station tribunal case, subsequent amendments to the tenure-review process stated rentals on leases should be set on pastoral values, not its potential for tourism.

Over a year on and Sue still finds it difficult to accept they've lost a large piece of the land they cared for over so many years, but she knows it was the right decision, amid a cloud of political uncertainty. 'John liked the pastoral lease system, but going forward we felt it wasn't as secure as it had been. The rental would have increased and we weren't sure at what point we wouldn't be able to afford it. By going into tenure review we thought it would give us a lot more security for future generations. For John and me, and probably for Grandma, it was a very bitter pill to have to swallow, but at the end of the day John and Randall accepted the deal that was put in front of us. The hardest thing to concede was the land between Cascade Hut and Aspiring Hut. It's not as productive as paddocks further down the valley, but we felt it was an important area, and the way we managed it kept it open and tidy for those entering into the national park. It's going to be interesting to see what happens now that there is a fence across the valley.'

Would the Aspinalls have considered selling the multi-million-dollar property and leaving the valley? 'Definitely not,' Sue maintains. 'It's way too precious. It didn't even enter our orbit.' Although the finer points of the review were negotiated in person by John and Randall, the decision to keep it in the family was a decision made collectively by all the family members. 'Selling was never on the cards,' Rachal says. 'Randall and Dad were always there to farm it. I don't care about how much it's worth, it is so much more important to me that it stays in the family as a farm. People at university used to get angry on my behalf that I was getting nothing, and my brother was getting the farm, but what they didn't understand was that I can still go back and visit there, and I can still call it home. And to know that Randall and Allison are there looking after it, well, to me that is much more valuable than anything else.

'It never really came into discussion selling it. The value and having grown up there and the privilege of living there is just worth so much more than any amount of money. Money is not going to give you the things that farm has given me, Randall and Catie. And with the history of what people have endured to get it to the state that it is today I would hate to not be able to say, "That's my home."'

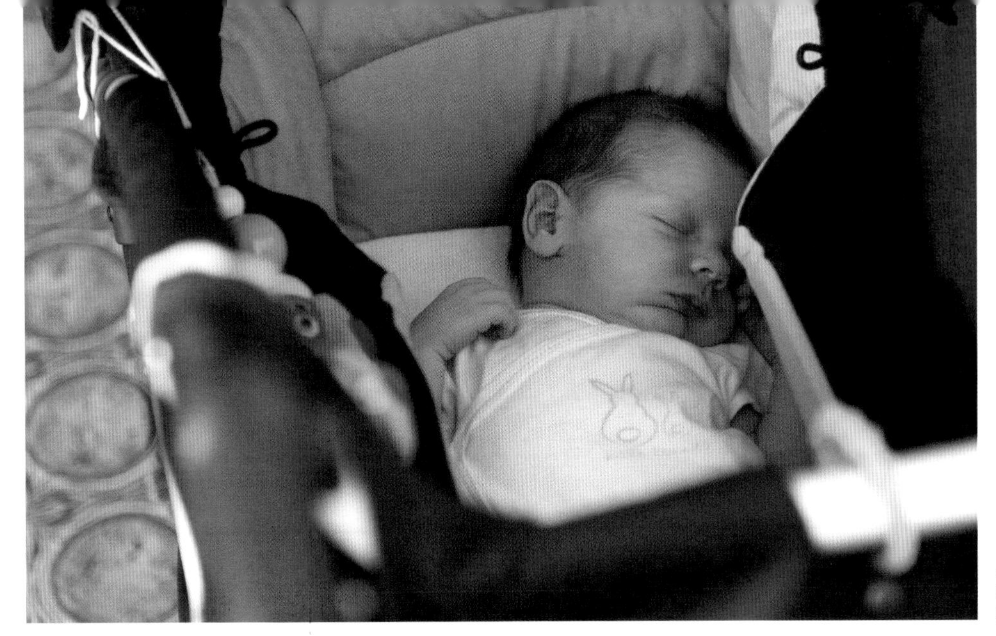

Johnny Aspinall at the Mt Aspiring Station homestead.

The debate over who the best custodians of the landscape might be will continue as more land is ceded to the Crown. Who are those that are best resourced to keep weeds and pests at bay, and who are those that are best positioned to make decisions on its future sustainability? John had always recognized the role of farmers in the control of weeds like hieracium, but as traditional livestock land continues to be turned over to the conservation estate, government resources will continue to be stretched.

One of the arguments put forward for freeholding land was to create opportunities for better land stewardship, but John believed well-managed leasehold land provided better landscape protection than the free market. 'There are always going to be some effects that are somewhat undesirable, but it's a question of balance and the pluses and minuses,' John said. 'I think people don't stop and realize the amount of management and management resource by the people who farm there in terms of weed and pest controlling. If we saw a gorse, a wilding pine, a broom bush, we kill them, whereas the agencies who currently manage these areas don't have the resources. They're not on the ground to the extent we are. They just don't have the ability to be here to monitor as closely what's happening on the land. We're always here.'

There are firm views on both sides of the argument and at times neither side is as well informed as it should be, but if there was an 'exhibit A' in favour of retaining the leasehold system, placing the guardianship of the high country's iconic landscapes with an intergenerational farmer, it must surely be Mt Aspiring Station and the Aspinall family.

Despite the sadness with which the Aspinalls ceded custodianship of 75 per cent of Mt Aspiring Station, their legacy in these hills will remain strong, and with Johnny Aspinall a new generation is born, a new voice in the valley with the weight and expectations of his forebears behind him. It is the latest chapter in a remarkable story of living in the Matukituki, face to face with nature, where an enduring pattern of life prevails and robust virtues still thrive.

MT ASPIRING
DESCRIPTION OF CONTENTS
ALBS
BALE No.
128
SSERS STAMP
CLOSE BOTTOM TWO FLAPS

MT ASPIRING STATION

Appendix

Eggs on Sundays – recipes from a back country valley

Despite the isolated existence the Aspinalls have lived in the Matukituki Valley, Mt Aspiring Station has always had a reputation for wholesome cooking. Cold meat and potato was a perennial favourite, mutton a staple, and eggs on Sundays a long-held tradition. And over the years farm workers and visitors to this back country station have often been surprised by the curious and diverse meals served up in the homestead kitchen.

It was always important to Phyllis that everyone who turned up when the gong sounded was properly fed. The following recipes are from her own handwritten cookbooks, compiled and passed on to the next generations, garnered from neighbours, lectures from the Women's Division of Federated Farmers, the Home Science Extension Service to rural New Zealand, herb societies, her own experiments and time-honoured hand-me-downs. Several were published in local community recipe books, others passed on in the hope that they would make life easier for those taking over the Aspiring kitchen.

Aspiring Onion Soup

at least 4 very large onions
50 g butter
1 tablespoon flour
1 litre meat stock
salt to taste
grated cheese

Peel onions and chop into small pieces. Cook gently in butter but do not brown. Blend in flour, then add stock. Stir till mixture boils, then cook gently, covered, for 30 minutes. Adjust seasoning. Serve with grated cheese.

Excellent for weary people too tired to eat, or if they are chilled. Onions are good for those with bronchial troubles, and would comfort a sufferer of a bad cold.

To Cream Clover Honey

Add 3 tablespoons of warmed creamed honey into 6 kg containers of runny honey and stir daily. Keep at an even temperature until creamed (14°C is the ideal temperature to cream honey, although the creaming works between 12–16°C). It will take four days.

As the room temperature drops (we do ours in autumn) it gets harder to stir and the colour changes to a smooth cream colour. I stir it once a day with a long plastic rod.

My measurements vary depending on how much creamed honey I have left over each year. I have to remember to keep some aside. I think it is the way of adding the warmed creamed honey into the runny honey, and the room temperature that are the key things.

Good luck and happy stirring!
Sue L Aspinall

Vichyssoise

2 cups finely chopped leeks (using white parts)
½ cup chopped onion
1 tablespoon butter
1 litre boiling water
5 medium chopped, peeled potatoes
2 teaspoons salt
2 cups milk
2 cups thin cream
chopped chives and parsley

Cook leeks and onion in butter till soft but not browned. Add water, potatoes and salt, and boil till tender (about 30 minutes). Sieve the mixture, or whizz in a blender. Return to pan, add milk and cream. Heat through but do not boil. Serve with a teaspoon of finely chopped chives and parsley mixture in the centre of each plate.

I use evaporated milk, which gives a velvety texture, but fewer calories. This is a classic chilled soup, but since we dislike cold soups we have never sampled it cold. One day if you feel daring, it's worth a try!

Cucumber Soup

2 cups grated cucumber
¼ cup grated onion
2 teaspoons salt
½ teaspoon pepper
1 litre chicken stock
2 tablespoons lemon juice

Combine all ingredients except lemon juice and simmer for 15 minutes. Add 2 tablespoons of lemon juice. Serve hot or cold. Tomato purée added to this is a good change, or extends it for a second day! Light and refreshing.

Raspberry Acid Royal

tartaric acid
water
2.25 litres fresh fruit (any of strawberries, loganberries, redcurrants, blackcurrants, blackberries and mulberries)
sugar

Dissolve 65 g tartaric acid in 1 litre of water and pour over the fruit. Let stand for 24 hours. Strain through a sieve and add 700 g sugar to each half litre of juice. Let it stand until sugar is dissolved, stirring at intervals. Bottle when sugar is dissolved. Seal down with corks. Dip the corked ends in melted paraffin wax if you wish, and this will keep for several years.

To the fruit that remains add 1 litre of boiling water to 25 g of tartaric acid and proceed as before, adding 550 g sugar to each half litre of juice. This will keep for 6 months, so set these bottles on the front of the shelf and allow the family to accumulate a good supply of vitamins!

Orange and Raisin Chutney

1.8 kg cooking apples
450 g blue raisins
2 oranges
850 ml malt vinegar
900 g sugar

Peel and core apples. Mince these with the raisins. Take a very thin skin from the oranges without any white and slice finely. Squeeze orange juice. Cook apples, raisins and orange rind with half of the vinegar in a covered pan till the apples are soft. Dissolve the sugar in the remainder of the vinegar and add with orange juice to the apple mixture. Reduce liquid with the lid off the pan until the desired consistency is obtained. Pot and cover in the usual way.

This excellent recipe has two big advantages. There is no onion, an asset for those who cannot eat it, and the chutney is ready to use immediately. It need not be matured the usual 3 months. Indeed, it is best used within a year of making, to keep the flavours fresh and interesting.

Flavoured Butter

Any of the following are great to eat on toast, sandwiches, savouries, grills or baked potatoes. They taste wonderful, yet are little effort to prepare. Any of these butters keep in a covered container in the refrigerator as long as ordinary butter.

Garlic Butter

100 g softened butter
1 clove garlic, crushed or finely chopped
generous squeeze lemon juice

The butter should be soft, as for creaming. Mix everything and stand at room temperature 2 hours before using. This blends the flavours.

OPEN
ATLAS

Herb Butter

100 g softened butter
1 tablespoon fresh herbs, finely chopped (e.g. parsley, summer savory, thyme, basil or tarragon)
generous squeeze lemon juice

Mix everything and stand at room temperature 2 hours before using. Should you need to use dried leaves, ½ teaspoon is ample.

Curry Butter

100 g softened butter
1 heaped teaspoon curry powder

Add curry powder to softened butter. Stand 2 hours at room temperature.

Celery Butter

100 g softened butter
½ teaspoon celery seed

Add celery seed to softened butter. Stand 2 hours at room temperature.

Horseradish Butter

100 g softened butter
1 heaped tablespoon prepared horseradish

Add horseradish to softened butter. Blend well and stand 2 hours at room temperature.

Mustard Butter

100 g softened butter
¼ cup prepared mustard

Add prepared mustard to softened butter, depending on how strongly flavoured you like it. Stand 2 hours at room temperature.

Lemon and Rosemary Mustard

- 2 cups yellow mustard seed
- 2 cups cider vinegar
- ½ cup red wine vinegar
- 2 tablespoons minced fresh rosemary
- grated zest 2 lemons
- 2 teaspoons sea salt
- 1½ tablespoons brown sugar

Soak the mustard seed in vinegars for 24 to 48 hours. Then add remaining ingredients and process all in the blender. Bottle, seal and keep in the fridge. Use within a few weeks.

Mixed Herb Vinegar

- 3–4 sprays thyme
- 3 sprays savory
- 4 sprigs mint
- 2–3 sprigs rosemary
- 2 sticks celery
- 6 shallots
- 1 parsley root, well washed, use foliage too
- 12 crushed white peppercorns
- 1 litre white wine vinegar

Bruise herbs and finely chop the celery, shallots and parsley plant. Put in a covered jar with peppercorns. Steep 3 weeks in vinegar. Shake occasionally. Strain and bottle.

The Very Best Dressing

- 4 tablespoons skim milk powder
- 1 meagre teaspoon mustard
- 1 meagre teaspoon salt
- ⅓ cup sugar
- vinegar

Mix dry ingredients to a cream with warm water. Add 2–3 tablespoons of vinegar, which will thicken it.

Dilute with whipped cream for a party. Vary with herbs, chutney or flavoured vinegar. I do four recipes, add 1 tin of evaporated milk, then use it as it comes.

Cucumber Mint Relish

- 2 large cucumbers, peeled and diced
- ⅓ cup chopped mint leaves
- ¼ cup vinegar
- 1 tablespoon sugar
- 2 teaspoons salt
- ¼ teaspoon pepper

Mix all ingredients with a tablespoon of water. Cover and chill. Keep covered in fridge. Use within a week. Very useful.

Green Mansion Slaw

- 1 head cabbage, cleaned and finely shredded
- ½ cup green grapes
- ½ cup pineapple pieces, drained
- ½ cup shredded cucumber

Mix all together.

Jerry's Pancakes

- 1 egg
- 2 cups milk
- 2 cups flour
- 3 tablespoons sugar
- 3 tablespoons baking powder
- ½ teaspoon salt

Beat egg and milk together. Sift dry ingredients and beat into egg and milk mixture. Have lightly greased frying pan heated. Pour about ⅔ cup of the mixture into the hot pan. When one side is golden, toss over and brown the other side. Serve flat with honey, golden syrup, jam or, best of all, a sprinkling of sugar and squeeze of lemon juice. Vanilla essence or ¼ cup coconut make interesting additions. Using a 20 cm frying pan, seven pancakes are made. A light snack for two boys.

Venison with Madeira Sauce

1 leg venison
fat for roasting
fat for larding
2 carrots, sliced
1 onion, sliced
½ lemon, thinly sliced
1 bay leaf
1 tablespoon flour
1 glass Madeira or red wine
stock or water
seasoning

Remove tough skin from meat, make little cuts in the surface and fill these with fat; venison is apt to be dry, and this will help to moisten it. Put in a covered roasting tin with fat, carrots, onion, lemon and bay leaf. Cook slowly for 2–2½ hours till tender and put on plate to keep hot. Skim fat from juices. Stir flour into the juice, blended with a small glass of Madeira and add stock or water to give the right consistency. Season as required and serve with slices of venison. This is delicious hot or cold.

William's Favourite

mutton chops
flour
1 small onion, finely chopped
grated rind 1 small orange
1 teaspoon finely chopped green ginger
1 dessertspoon soy sauce
salt
3 peppercorns

Cut the ribs from mutton into suitable small pieces. Place dry (that is, without fat or water) in a covered casserole, and cook in a moderate oven for 1½ hours. By now the meat should be almost cooked, and the surplus fat melted. Remove from casserole and keep hot. Drain fat, but leave juice to make gravy. Blend flour into the juice, and add water till the desired consistency has been reached. Stir over heat till the mixture boils, add the chopped onion or shallots, orange rind, green ginger, soy sauce, salt and peppercorns, and the pieces of meat. Return to the oven and cook gently till the meat is ready. Serve with baked potatoes and green vegetables.

Note on green ginger: this can be bought from the greengrocer during autumn and early winter. I then keep my treasure in the fridge, but it could equally well be stored in dry sherry. Use about 1 teaspoon finely chopped in soup or meat dishes. Delicious!

Poacher's Pot

- 700 g oven-ready whole rabbit
- 1 level tablespoon cornflour
- 25 g butter
- 100 g onion, chopped
- 2 level tablespoons demerara sugar
- 1 level teaspoon tomato paste
- 2 level teaspoons mustard powder
- 500 ml stock
- 3 tablespoons soy sauce
- 1 tablespoon lemon juice
- salt and ground pepper

Wipe the rabbit and cut into 12 pieces. Toss rabbit pieces in cornflour. Melt butter in a large, deep frying pan and brown rabbit pieces well. Remove from pan and keep to one side. Sauté onion in the same frying pan until transparent, then stir in sugar, tomato paste, mustard and stock. Bring to the boil, reduce heat, then add remaining ingredients and rabbit. Cover pan and simmer gently for 1¼ hours until tender. Serve on a bed of freshly boiled rice.

Sue Aspinall's Baked Chops

- 6 mutton chops
- 2 cups fresh breadcrumbs
- 1 large onion, chopped
- 1 teaspoon green herb stock
- ½ teaspoon garlic powder
- 1 egg
- salt and pepper
- 2 teaspoons beef stock (powder)
- 1 cup boiling water
- 1 tablespoon Worcestershire sauce
- 2 tablespoons tomato sauce

Lightly brown chops and place in a large oven roasting dish. Mix breadcrumbs, chopped onion, herb stock, garlic, egg, salt and pepper as stuffing. A little milk may need to be added. Place a good spoonful of stuffing on top of each chop. Mix beef stock with boiling water and sauces and pour over chops. Bake at 150°C for 2 hours.

Angels and Devils on Horseback

bacon in thin slices
1 tin smoked oysters (assuming fresh oysters are not available)
pitted prunes
toothpicks

Cut bacon, without rind, into strips just long enough to encircle each oyster or prune. As each one is made, spear with a toothpick, arrange in a single layer in ovenware dish and grill lightly. These savouries can be prepared, placed on tinfoil dishes and frozen till required for cooking.

Dutch Potatoes

3 large potatoes
1 small onion, chopped
1 tablespoon butter
2 tablespoons parsley
salt and pepper

Peel and dice potatoes. Cook chopped onions in butter until slices are golden brown. Add potatoes, parsley and seasoning. Barely cover with water. Cook until potatoes are tender. Most of the water will be absorbed by now. Sprinkle over a little chopped parsley and seasonings. Very good for lunch on a cold day with cold meat.

Curried Egg Spread

4 eggs, hard-boiled and shelled
½ cup salad dressing
½ teaspoon curry powder
2 teaspoons homemade mustard
1 teaspoon finely mashed chutney

Cut the hard-boiled eggs into slices. Mix the remaining ingredients together. Mix eggs and curry mixture to make spread. For a picnic you could serve this with lettuce leaves and raw vegetables. Alternatively, cut eggs into wedges then serve with a slice of cucumber, wedge of tomato and a little radish or pickled onion impaled on a toothpick, with the curry mixture.

This is a good recipe. You could use it for ordinary scones or, for a crowd, cut bigger rounds to serve individually. Filled and decorated they can look very special.

Potato Patties

leftover mashed potato
leftover meat (optional)
1 egg
parsley, chopped
flour
salt and pepper
fat or oil for frying

Use leftover mashed potato. If there is a little leftover meat it is a good addition. Blend smooth potato with beaten egg. Add plenty of chopped parsley and a little flour. Season. Shape into patties, using about 2 tablespoons of mixture for each one, and fry in shallow fat or oil. Serve with gravy or sauce. Since potato greatly varies I can't give amounts, but the mixture should hold together, not crumble apart!

Kai Si Ming

1 onion, chopped
450 g mince
3 cups water
1 packet chicken noodle soup
1 tablespoon curry powder
1 tablespoon mixed herbs
200 g sliced green beans or ½ shredded cabbage

Brown the onion, add the mince, then water, chicken noodle soup, curry powder, mixed herbs and green beans or cabbage. Cook for about 40 minutes, stirring from time to time. This is a wonderful stretchy meal, and can be made in vast quantities for a crowd.

The Staff of Life – Bermaline Loaf

1½ cups plain flour
1½ cups wholemeal flour
3 teaspoons baking powder
1 tablespoon golden syrup
milk

Mix dry ingredients with golden syrup and milk to form a wet dough. Put into a loaf tin. Only have tin half full; a 5 lb (2.5 kg) honey tin is great. Cook for 1 hour in a moderate oven.

When making this, I put a second recipe of dry ingredients in an airtight jar. The next load can then be made very quickly, with additions of syrup and milk.

Burmese Rice

25 g butter
1 tablespoon curry powder
5 tomatoes, peeled and chopped
salt and pepper
100 g cooked rice
1 tablespoon grated cheese
parsley

Melt the butter and add the curry powder. Cook a little then add tomatoes and seasoning. Simmer for 10 minutes. Add cooked rice and cheese. Heat mixture thoroughly, but don't boil after adding the cheese. Garnish with parsley.

A fresh, appetizing flavour.

Bryce's Marinade

½ cup cooking oil
juice of 2 lemons
2 bay leaves
1 teaspoon finely chopped green ginger
2 cloves garlic, crushed
grated rind ½ orange
salt and pepper

Mix all ingredients together. Place meat in a suitable plastic bag with this marinade, cover closely, and refrigerate.

Meat: Cubes of shoulder mutton or leg of mutton are suitable. Turn bag, or move plastic surface gently with the fingers four times a day to coat all meat pieces with marinade. It can be used and be flavoured after 4 hours, but will keep refrigerated for up to 2 days. The meat will have an improved flavour and will also become more tender.

Cook meat in marinade, in a casserole, when wanted. It does not require additional flavouring, but should be thickened in the usual way, or by placing 2 tablespoons sage in the mixture before cooking. Serve with green vegetables or a tossed salad.

Station Brownie

450 g sultanas
2 cups sugar
2 cups water
2 tablespoons butter
1 tablespoon syrup or honey
675 g flour
1 teaspoon baking soda
1 teaspoon ginger
½ teaspoon cinnamon
½ teaspoon cloves
1 teaspoon mixed spice
1 teaspoon salt

Boil the fruit, sugar, water, butter and syrup or honey together, then cool. Stir occasionally to blend the sugar. Mix the dry ingredients together and have ready in a large bowl. Mix wet and dry ingredients. Cook in greased or papered tins, for 1 to 1½ hours.

Scrunch

50 g butter
½ cup raw sugar
2 cups cornflakes

Melt the butter in a generous-sized saucepan. Remove from heat and stir in sugar, then stir in cornflakes.

This is a fine embellishment for fruit and ice cream dessert. The family and most others enjoy it greatly. Should some remain after the meal, store in an airtight container.

When a friend first acquired an electric frypan, her husband declared that she cooked everything but Cornies and ice cream in it, so I hastened to send this recipe!

John Aspinall's Truffles

125 g soft butter
125 g caster sugar
2 heaped tablespoons cocoa
8 dates, chopped
½ cup sultanas
½ cup chopped walnuts
1½ cups coconut

Beat butter and caster sugar together in a bowl. Then add the cocoa. Mix well, then add the dates, sultanas and walnuts. (You could use any other dried or crystallized fruit chopped finely, such as raisins, ginger, cherries or crystallized pineapple.) Shake about 1 cup coconut on a flat plate, and have more alongside. Take teaspoon lots of the mixture, drop on the coconut. When you have about six little lumps, roll in the coconut, then with the hands, till they are round. Restrain yourself from licking your fingers till all are rolled in balls. Hide in the fridge for an hour, then keep in the back of a cupboard until you want to eat some with after-dinner coffee. They will keep in the freezer or in an airtight tin for several weeks.

It's best to make this recipe when your mother isn't looking. She might object to all her goodies being used at once.

Christopher's Half-hour Pudding

½ cup sultanas
1 cup flour
2 teaspoons baking powder
1 teaspoon salt
milk
2 cups water
¼ teaspoon nutmeg
2 tablespoons butter
1 cup brown sugar

Add sultanas in a generous ovenware bowl to the flour, baking powder and salt. Add milk and mix to make scone dough. Meanwhile boil together the water with nutmeg, butter and brown sugar. Stir occasionally to ensure sugar dissolves. Pour boiling hot syrup over scone dough and bake 30 minutes at 350°C. Serve hot.

Jack Aspinall's Macaroons

1 cup sugar
⅓ cup water
1 egg white
375 g coconut

Mix the sugar and water into a thick syrup. Beat the egg white very stiff, then with your third hand, drizzle a fine thread of the syrup into this, beating constantly. Add coconut and form into balls. Cook in a slow oven till the surface is dried and golden brown.

Jack was known as a fine cook, but nobody ever saw a written recipe.

Felixstowe Tart

- 75 g butter
- 30 g sugar
- 1 or 2 egg yolks
- 90 g flour
- 90 g cornflour
- 1 teaspoon baking powder
- milk
- raspberry jam
- egg whites
- sugar

Cream the butter and sugar. Add eggs and dry ingredients. Mix with milk to make a light dough. Spread in a greased cake tin. Bake, and when cooled a little spread with raspberry jam, and a meringue made from egg white, beaten with 2 tablespoons of sugar added for each white. Spread over top and brown lightly. The base cooks in a hot oven in about 20 minutes.

To Soften Socks

- 2 tablespoons vinegar
- handful of salt

Mix vinegar and salt. Add cold water to barely cover socks. Let soak for at least 1 hour.

Wallpaper Cleaner

Slices of stale white bread, brushed downwards, moved lightly over wallpaper.

Excellent Window Cleaner

Mix equal quantities of kerosene, ammonia, methylated spirits and water. Shake well in a bottle before using. Rub on window with a cloth and rub off immediately with a soft cloth. This isn't hard to do and makes windows sparkle!

Oven Cleaner

- 3 teaspoons baking soda
- 1 cup water
- 1 tablespoon vinegar

Put all ingredients into a saucepan and bring to the boil. Brush this liquid onto the cold oven. Heat oven to 180°C. Allow to cool. Wipe out with a damp cloth.

Bottle Cleaner

Crush an egg shell and drop in the bottle. Add a little hot water and swill around. This will get rid of discolouration.

Rich Hand Lotion

- 1 teaspoon clear honey
- 1 teaspoon essential oil of lavender
- 2 tablespoons almond oil
- 2 tablespoons sesame oil
- 1 tablespoon glycerine and rose water

Melt honey. Whisk with oils and glycerine and rose water. Cap securely in an airtight bottle. This is an excellent lotion to help chapped hands and those damaged by a busy period in the garden.

Acknowledgements

A special thank you to Sue Aspinall for her incredible support from the day I stepped off a bus in Wanaka through to the final proofs. Sue, I admire your energy, tender heart and remarkable fortitude. I would also like to thank Randall and Allison for their hospitality and famous Aspinall patience, and the rest of the Aspinall family — Rachal, Catie, Julia, Christopher, Willie and Phyllis — for sharing memories of the good times and bad, the tough times and all that they hold dear. I would also like to thank the cast of characters that lit up the Matukituki Valley: Paul Blackgrove, Gary and Mike Walker, Florence Gaud and Kerie Uren, Struan Mehrtens, Monique King, Richie and Bev Dick; and to the Wanaka community, Heather and Stu Thorne, Phil Melchior, Geoff Wayatt and Paul Hellebrekers. Not least, I would like to thank the team at HarperCollins: Bill Honeybone, Antoinette Sturny, Alison Brook, Sandra Noakes, Lorraine Steele and Cheryl Rowe; as well as the following people for their important contributions: Emily Crofoot, Lorain Day, Kieran Scott, Danilo Hegg, Russell Lambeth, Jeremy Silva, Chris Lumsden, Brent Pihama, Mike Paardekooper, Pamela Simpson, Martyn Myer and Tom Donald. Lastly, to Lara Trimming for her tolerance and understanding and, as always, my father David and mother Jenny for their perennial encouragement.

Alex Hedley is a writer, photographer and commissioning editor based in Auckland. He published *Fernleaf Cairo: The Fascinating Story of New Zealanders in Wartime Egypt* in 2009, and was the photographer of 2011 title *Castlepoint: The Story of Life on an Iconic New Zealand Sheep and Cattle Station*, both published by HarperCollins.